Joe Van Wormer was born in the Ozarks, grew up in Florida, attended the University of Missouri, and became a Certified Public Accountant. He gave this up to edit house organs for a trucking firm and a lumber mill in Oregon, where he began to use, in his words, "very little trucking material and a lot of wildlife stuff. The experts all said I was crazy, but the readers loved it . . . the board of directors didn't."

Since then, he has devoted his time to free-lance photography and writing about wildlife and nature, and has contributed six books to the Living World series.

Now he writes, "Recently we moved onto an acre of ground in Oregon's Willamette Valley. It is half lawn and half weed patch. The lawn is for us and the weed patch for the birds. Our neighbors think we should grow vegetables but I explain that that's my bird garden. We haven't been here long and they are not right sure about us."

THE WORLD OF THE AMERICAN ELK

LIVING WORLD BOOKS

John K. Terres, Editor

The World of the American Elk by Joe Van Wormer

The World of the Ant by David F. Costello

The World of the Beaver by Leonard Lee Rue III

The World of the Bison by Ed Park

The World of the Black Bear by Joe Van Wormer

The World of the Bobcat by Joe Van Wormer

The World of the Canada Goose by Joe Van Wormer

The World of the Coyote by Joe Van Wormer

The World of the Frog and the Toad by George Porter

The World of the Great Horned Owl
    by G. Ronald Austing and John B. Holt, Jr.

The World of the Grizzly Bear by W. J. Schoonmaker

The World of the Opossum by James F. Keefe
    with photographs by Don Wooldridge

The World of the Porcupine by David F. Costello

The World of the Pronghorn by Joe Van Wormer

The World of the Raccoon by Leonard Lee Rue III

The World of the Red Fox by Leonard Lee Rue III

The World of the Red-tailed Hawk by G. Ronald Austing

The World of the White-tailed Deer by Leonard Lee Rue III

The World of the Wolf by Russell J. Rutter and
    Douglas H. Pimlott

The World of the Woodchuck by W. J. Schoonmaker

The World of the
American Elk

Text and Photographs by
Joe Van Wormer

J. B. LIPPINCOTT COMPANY
Philadelphia and New York

To Scott Joseph Miles

Contents

The World of the American Elk

Meet the American Elk

THE FIRST BULL ELK I ever saw got up from his bed in a timber thicket and chased me. He was a big handsome animal, and, because it was late September, his coat was in its prime. His great antlers, six points on a side, polished and lethal-looking, seemed too large for him to carry. Bedded down nearby was his harem of eight cows, along with four of their calves.

The first bull elk I ever saw.

I had traveled a thousand miles to Yellowstone National Park to see and photograph elk and other animals. Although I had made it a point to be able to recognize an elk when I saw one, I must confess that at that time I knew little about them. I didn't, for example, know enough to give a bull elk plenty of room during the mating season.

A mature bull in prime physical condition, with massive widespread antlers reaching upward four or more feet above his head, is in my opinion the most magnificent animal on the American continent. When this bull rose from his bed and started for me, he seemed about fifteen feet tall. I didn't wait to see how serious his intentions were but beat a hasty and somewhat undignified retreat to my car. From this safe vantage point I watched the great beast, now poised at the edge of the timber. After a few moments he turned back toward his waiting cows and with great dignity disappeared among the trees.

The following day I returned to the same spot and discovered that the bull and his harem had moved to a meadow bordering Yellowstone's Madison River a short distance west of Madison Junction. The bull was resting on a slight elevation fifty feet off the road. His "wives" were in the meadow near the river, some resting, some grazing. I parked at a discreet distance and prepared to watch for a while.

Soon a small car came along. Its young driver saw me parked, swung in behind to see what the attraction was—a common occurrence in Yellowstone—and, camera in hand, jumped out of the car and walked toward the elk. By the time I got my car window down to warn him, he was standing ten feet in front of the bull and squinting through the camera's view finder. After the shutter clicked, he walked past me back to his car, grinned happily, and said, "That is the biggest deer I ever saw!"

Why the bull elk took exception to my presence but tolerated an even closer approach by this fellow I did not understand. I tried to smooth my ruffled ego with the thought that the young man was probably confusing the elk with a mule deer.

This fine bull, probably six years old, has seven-point antlers.

Actually, the American elk *is* a member of the deer family. It is an even-toed hoofed mammal, or ungulate, in the order Artiodactyla,* the family Cervidae, the genus *Cervus,* or true deer, and the species *canadensis,* which means "of Canada." It has been misnamed, like some other mammals on this continent, notably the bison and the pronghorn, incorrectly called buffalo and antelope. Explorers and early

*The order Artiodactyla includes pigs, peccaries, hippopotamuses, camels, chevrotains, deer and their allies, giraffes, pronghorns, and the hollow-horned ruminants: wild sheep and goats and the North American bison. The family Cervidae—deer and allies—in North America includes the elk, or wapiti, the white-tailed and mule deer, the moose, and the caribou, or reindeer.—*The Editor.*

15

pioneers in America called this animal an elk despite the fact that in Europe and Asia this term was given to the European moose, which looks similar to the American moose. Although the confusion still exists and the name "elk" for this animal persists, the Shawnee Indian name "wapiti" is frequently used.

Ancestors of all deer apparently first appeared as small cat-sized animals some 45 million years ago, in the Oligocene. Antlers apparently evolved during Miocene times, about 35 million years ago. During the Pleistocene, or Ice Age (which began about a million years ago), the forerunners of today's American elk reached this country. During those thousands of years when much of this continent was covered with ice, a land bridge connected it with Asia and provided a crossing for many animal species, among them elk. The American elk left many relatives behind in Europe and Asia. Our elk resembles the red deer of Europe but really looks more like some Asiatic wapiti. The maral of the Caspian region, for example, could easily be mistaken for the American elk.

Early in the history of the United States, there was a total of six forms of elk in America that were named and described by scientists. According to Olaus J. Murie, in *The Elk of North America,* two of these were destroyed during this country's development and have long since become extinct. They were the eastern elk *(Cervus canadensis canadensis)* and the Merriam elk *(Cervus merriami)*. Another species, the tule elk *(Cervus nannodes),* of southern California, came within *one* breeding pair of meeting this same fate. Available information indicates that all the American subspecies, except the tule elk, looked very much alike. The tule elk, usually considered a separate species, is much smaller and paler than the others, with shorter legs and more white around its ears.

To compare the American elk with other game animals, it is the largest round-horned deer and, next to the moose, the largest living deer in the world. Bighorn sheep and mountain goats are more elusive; pronghorn are faster and more colorful; deer are smaller, more plenti-

"Monarch of the wild."

ful, and more graceful in their movements. But if any American animal deserves the title "monarch of the wild," it is the elk.

Elk are four or five times larger than deer. Mature bulls weigh from 500 to 1,000 pounds. I heard of one monster on Afognak Island in Alaska that weighed more than 1,500 pounds, but I think 700 pounds is probably a fair average. Mature cows average from 400 to 700 pounds. Weights vary during the year because elk usually lose weight in winter, when food is not plentiful.

The length of a mature elk from the tip of the nose to the tip of the tail is between 90 and 114 inches (7½ to 9½ feet). Shoulder height is from 54 to 60 inches (4½ to 5 feet). Cows are smaller than bulls. The tail is rather insignificant, about 5 inches long.

The head is slender and well proportioned; the ears are moderately large, with pointed tips. Usually, only the males have antlers, which first appear when the bulls are ten or eleven months old.

Normally, these first antlers are mere spikes, small in diameter, from 10 to 20 inches in length, and occasionally forked at the tips. However,

There is a marked difference in the antler growth of these two young males, both of them about a year old.

Long spikes with brow tines indicate that this is probably the second set of antlers but that the bull was not in very good physical condition during their growth.

The cup-shaped formation at the tip of these antlers, still in velvet, is characteristic of the Roosevelt elk. This one is about two years old.

there is considerable variation in this first set. The second set, which is still small and slender, ordinarily carries four or five points. The third set is likely to look much like the second set, with the same number of points, but heavier.

The fourth set, which appears when the animal is over four years old, generally has the six points considered normal for a typical mature bull. However, due to variations and inconsistencies in size, shape, and number of points, antler girth rather than number of points is a better indicator of the age of an elk.

Each antler of a prime set consists of a main beam that grows outward, upward, and backward, curving evenly inward toward the tip, and long, branching tines. The first tine, the one nearest the head, is called the *brow tine,* and it projects forward over the face. Next above is the *bay* or *bez tine,* which is about as long as the brow tine and also projects forward a short distance above it. The two brow and two bay tines on a set of antlers make formidable weapons called dog killers, war tines, or lifters. Projecting forward about midway up the main

19

This bull, probably three years old, has a well-developed set of four-point antlers.

Mature Rocky Mountain bulls. The one with the freakish-looking right antler may be a little beyond his prime.

The tines of six-point antlers are called: (a) brow tine; (b) bay, or bez, tine; (c) tray, or tres-, tine; (d) royal, or dagger, point; (e and f) sur-royals.

The antlers of this old bull are described as "palmated."

beam and generally shorter than the first two is the third tine, called the *tray* or *tres-tine.* The dominant tine is the fourth one, referred to as the *royal* or *dagger point.* Usually it is the longest, strongest, and deadliest. The last two points, which form the divided tip of the antler, are the *sur-royals.*

A bull with the normal complement of six points, or tines, per side is called a royal stag. One with seven points on each antler is called an imperial.

A prime set of antlers, which weighs between forty and fifty pounds, reaches full growth in only four months. Each antler averages about a half-inch a day! One might think that growing antlers would rob other bony structures in the body of minerals when the animal is in poor physical condition, but apparently antler growth gets second call on the available nutrients. Normal body needs come first.

Antlers become larger and finer until the bulls reach their seventh or eighth year. After that the animals are past their prime, and some freakishness may develop. Occasionally an antler will become palmated, somewhat like a moose antler, or extra points may appear. James A. Harper of the Oregon State Game Commission, who has made many studies of elk, reported seeing a mature bull that had a typical seven-point antler on one side and a single large spike on the other. As bulls grow older, their antlers actually diminish in size, and some very old bulls that have been killed had only spikes. A few cows are known to have produced antlers.*

Sets of antlers on younger bulls also show occasional freakishness. An abnormal number of points may be the result of an exceptional supply of antler-building food. On the other hand, poor physical condition may result in subnormal antlers.

Coloration of an elk varies with both the season and the species, but the color is basically brown: lighter on the sides and much darker, sometimes almost black, on the head, neck, legs, and under parts. Long dark hairs on the neck and throat form a mane, which is an elk characteristic. (Calves grow this mane during their first winter.) A ring of light brown, darker on the sides and lighter at top and bottom, surrounds each eye. A similar coloration is found on the chin, below which there is often a light brown streak that, in some specimens, looks like a goatee.

Following the dorsal line down to the rump patch is a strip of brown darker than the body but lighter than the mane. Bordering the patch is a black or dark-brown line somewhat darker at the bottom than at the top. The rump patch itself is tan, lighter than the rest of the animal but varying from almost white to rich tawny. The hoofs are usually black.

During the winter, coloring on the sides becomes quite light and appears almost white in contrast to the dark legs, neck, and head. This

*Olaus J. Murie reported seeing at least five cows that were antlered. Each bore a single spike. Several mounted heads of females with more complex antlers were owned by residents of Jackson Hole, Wyoming.—*The Editor.*

23

light coloring is more pronounced in older bulls than in cows, calves, and young bulls. In summer, the coloration is much darker, especially along the sides of the body, which is generally a glossy reddish brown. Then the mane is not so pronounced, and the legs, neck, and head are not so dark.

Albinism, though not unknown among elk, seems to occur rarely. It may be more common than observations show, because albino calves would be easier for predators to notice. Thus, they would not have too good a chance to grow up. Interestingly, several partial albinos have been reported. One, which was seen in 1947 in Prairie Creek State Park, California, had a half-brown, half-white head; oddly enough, the line between brown and white was as straight as if it had been deliberately ruled off.

Most of the reports of albinos I have found involve Oregon elk. Whether this is significant or not I have no way of knowing; and of course there may be many more in other areas that I have failed to find in the records. Three albinos were seen in Clatsop County, Oregon, in 1946—a spike bull, a yearling cow, and a calf. They were described as being a "light cream" color, with darker brown showing through on the head, neck, and legs. The following year, two calves of similar coloring were seen by an Oregon Game Commission biologist. Another Oregon albino elk, a cow, was reported to be fawn-colored with a white rump patch and pink eyes.

The rump patch of the elk resembles that of the pronghorn, but its function, if any, is obscure and seems relatively unimportant. The flashing white of the raised hair on a pronghorn's rump is a communication device, usually signaling danger. But among the thousands of elk I have watched and photographed there was only one that seemed to be able to raise the hairs of its rump patch. This was a calf approximately three and a half months old.

It has been suggested that the elk's rump patch is used to coordinate a moving herd or to give information about the position of distant

When flared, the pronghorn's white rump patch acts as a warning signal to other pronghorns.

animals. While this may be true, it would seem that, today at least, the importance of this information is not vital enough to the welfare of an elk herd to warrant having this contrasting patch. But it might very well be a carry-over from some ancient period when elk needed to use a flared rump patch as a built-in warning system.

Nevertheless, the elk's patch does perform one important function as far as man is concerned: it helps him to identify the species. It is difficult for me to imagine anyone confusing an elk with any other North American animal, although records show that mules and horses have been mistaken for elk and shot by hunters. Several years ago an elk hunter stopped in downtown Bend, Oregon, and proudly displayed a four-point bull "elk" he had killed. A passing game warden stopped to see the animal and promptly gave the hunter a citation. His "elk" was a large four-point mule deer buck, and the deer season was closed. *The elk is the only deer in this country with a tan rump patch and a tail to match.* Mule deer have a small white rump patch, but the tail

While the elk's tail and rump patch are tan, the mule deer, above, has a white, black-tipped tail. (National Audubon Society photo)

has a black tip or a black tip with black on top. White-tailed deer have dark body color on top of their white tails. Moose have no rump patch; nor do horses and mules.

Frustrated elk hunters I have talked to stoutly maintain that elk need no warning system other than their senses of hearing, smell, and sight, all of which seem to be extremely well developed. It is difficult to measure the development of these senses in wild animals, and probably the best sources of information are the reports of competent observers. There is evidence that the sense of smell is probably most important to elk. They seem to be able to identify other elk by scent. The smell of an enemy, human or otherwise, creates an instant alert that is usually accompanied by immediate flight.

Their hearing may be equally sensitive, although not so discriminatory. Even though other noises might seem to mask it, a strange noise will cause elk to head for safer country. I observed this firsthand while photographing these animals in Prairie Creek State Park in northwestern California. The western boundary of the park is the Pacific Ocean. High bluffs covered with big timber extend along the coast in

26

As this picture shows, elk have well-developed senses of sight and smell, and are thus hard to take by surprise.

this area. Between the bluffs and the ocean there is a strip of beach from 100 to 200 yards wide. About three-quarters of this strip is covered with grass, weeds, and brush. The quarter nearest the ocean is sand and driftwood. Along this strip, both cows and bulls have always permitted me to get within reasonable telephoto range if I didn't make too much of a fuss while approaching them. These are, of course, protected animals, but even so there is a limit to how close an approach they will tolerate.

As might be expected in an area exposed to the Pacific Ocean, there is a constant background roar of wind and surf. Despite this I often noticed a reaction to the quiet click of the camera shutter. Once, when I inadvertently banged a tripod leg against the car, the high-pitched metallic sound caused a small panic as the herd jumped and ran for a few yards. An unfamiliar sound is all the warning they need. And generally they don't wait around to see what made it.

I saw another example of their alertness and sensitivity to sound in this same area while follownig a fine five-point bull through thick

27

This small herd was able to catch the sound of my clicking camera above the roar of the surf.

growth on a hillside. This was no stalk, for the bull knew where I was all the time. I was just moving at a slow, easy pace, hoping he would permit me to get and stay within camera range. The animal fed slowly along as I worked my way closer to him. He didn't seem to be paying any attention to me. It took me a few minutes to realize that, although I thought I was drawing closer, he was remaining the same distance away! I got no closer than his tolerance limit, which was a distance of about ten yards, but this was better than I had expected. In fact, it was about as close as I wanted to get. When I stopped moving toward him, he stopped moving away from me.

After feeding for a few minutes he moved uphill into a small clearing and lay down in a patch of sunlight. I followed, taking pictures as I went. While I stood there in the clearing wondering what to do next, the bull closed his eyes and apparently dozed. I decided to ease around the edge of the clearing and find a new camera angle above him. The soft, moist earth deadened the sound of my movements, but that first shutter click coming from a different direction alarmed him. He opened his eyes, looked straight at me, and then got up and headed down the hill, too fast for me to follow.

Elk have keen eyesight, and they seemingly are able to detect movement, especially movement alien to their environment, at considerable distances. On the other hand, motionless objects, such as a man sitting quietly on a stump, may go undetected. Many elk are killed by hunters who have the patience to sit for hours.

The elk is not a particularly fast animal, which no doubt explains why it prefers to rely upon dense cover for concealment and protection. Estimates of its top speed vary from 28 to 45 miles an hour, but a speed of 30 to 35 miles seems more widely accepted. Its usual gait is a slow, stately walk; when disturbed, it may trot with its muzzle held at the horizontal or slightly above. Its gallop is similar to that of many other hoofed animals.

Elk have an amazing ability to jump over objects and can clear a

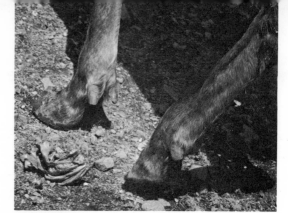

The elk's dew claws are clearly visible on the hoofs.

Elk sign: a track and, at lower right, a pellet-shaped dropping.

seven-foot wooden fence without much trouble. Generally such jumps are made from a standing rather than a running position. The elk's long, powerful legs terminate in evenly paired toes; the tips of the two middle ones are encased in horny hoofs. Behind these and raised off the ground are a pair of small lateral hoofs called dew claws. They aid in traveling through soft mud or snow.

Elk tracks are larger and rounder than those of deer and somewhat smaller and less pointed than those of moose. Adult elk tracks are from 4 to 4½ inches long. That size alone distinguishes them from deer, although elk calves leave smaller tracks than adults. However, even these will be more rounded than those of deer. Elk and moose, or elk and cattle, using the same range leave tracks that can be difficult to distinguish, especially if there are any young cattle. Adult cattle leave

The elk's lachrymal gland, forward and slightly below the eye, is quite noticeable.

large and blocky tracks, but with young cattle around, other signs, such as droppings, may be needed to identify the maker of a track.

When walking, an elk places his hind foot on the spot the forefoot has just vacated. The distance between the point where the same foot strikes the ground is from 50 to 60 inches in a walk and from 8 to 14 feet in a gallop.

Elk have two pairs of external glands. The lachrymal gland is forward and slightly below the eye and is quite noticeable. The metatarsal gland is below the hock on the outside of the hind leg. Interdigital glands between the toes and tarsal glands inside the hind legs are not present.

American elk browse a wide variety of shrubs and eat grasses and forbs, which are herbaceous plants that are not grasses, or grasslike. They vary their diets according to foods that are available. Basically, they

31

are grazers and prefer grass at all times of the year. They show definite preferences for certain plants, and this changes with the season, partly as a result of what is available and partly because some plants ripen and die and are then less palatable.

In general, elk are found on ranges where three quite different kinds of weather predominate. Probably any of the subspecies could get along on the foods available in any of the areas; nevertheless, the plants each consumes are different because their range climates vary.

Elk in the coastal areas eat orchard grass, sweet vernal grass, redtop, California oat grass, perennial rye grass, and slough grass, among others. Favorites of the Rocky Mountain elk include needle grass, bluegrass, wheat grass, and sedge grass. These elk also have a wide choice of browse plants available to them. Included are fir needles, Rocky Mountain maple, serviceberry, sagebrush, bog birch, ceanothus, mountain mahogany, rabbit brush, juniper, mistletoe, pine, quaking aspen, chokecherry, bitter brush, currant bush, huckleberry, willow, wild rose, and the acorns, leaves, and twigs of oaks.

Roosevelt elk in the Olympic range and in Oregon's coastal range depend more on browse than do those in California; next to grass it is the most important item in their diet. Some of these foods, not necessarily in the order of preference, seasonally or otherwise, are salmonberry, huckleberry, maple, vine maple, devil's-club, deer fern, sword fern, blackberry, willow, salal, red alder, mountain ash, California wild rose, western red cedar, Douglas fir, and western hemlock. The foliage of these last three items is generally out of reach of elk, but any fallen limbs or branches are usually trimmed closely.

In the Olympics, elk also eat a considerable amount of lichens of a kind commonly found on the trunks and limbs of trees in the upper Transition and Canadian zones that are referred to as "gray moss." They have also been seen feeding on the fibrous pulp in partially decayed logs. John E. Schwartz, in an Olympic elk study for the U. S. Forest Service, reported that this pulp is much sought after, especially from cottonwood, hemlock, spruce, big-leaf maple, and vine maple. On Afognak Island in Alaska, elk were found eating mushrooms. Fungi have also been reported as a preferred food in the Olympics.

Depending upon its size, an elk will stretch between five and seven feet to obtain food. It does not show much inclination to stand on its hind legs and reach higher. In normal feeding, the herd moves slowly along in one general direction.

It has been estimated that an elk consumes slightly more than 21 pounds of grass each day. This is a little less than the poundage supplied to captive elk in one zoo; that totaled 27 pounds—20 of alfalfa hay and 7 of pellets. In this same zoo, spring rations were cut to 15 and 5 pounds, respectively, as a good supply of grass was available.

In *The Elk of Jackson Hole,* Chester C. Anderson reported the results of a feeding experiment at Jackson Hole, Wyoming, designed to determine the amount of food necessary for the elk herd that winters there on the National Elk Refuge. From the experiment it was concluded that 11.4 pounds of forage an animal was needed each day. This was apparently merely a sustaining diet, for during the forty-three days of this experiment calves lost an average of a bit over a half pound per day, while adult elk lost an average of about a pound and a quarter per day. Calves ate a significantly higher amount of feed per hundred pounds of body weight than did the adults.

Elk are attracted to so-called "salt licks," places where wild animals lick salt that occurs naturally on the ground. This is somewhat of a misnomer, however; they might more accurately be called "mineral licks," for they do not always contain common salt. Lick samples from northwestern Wyoming contain calcium, magnesium, sulphate, phosphate, and only minute traces of chlorides.

In Olympic National Park elk commonly use natural mineral licks in the north and east portions of the park; they ignore salt blocks placed on the west side by the U. S. Forest Service. The reasons for this are not known, but the best explanation seems to be that ocean salt is

A two-year-old bull elk chews his cud during a midday rest.

carried inshore to the west side of the park by wind-blown spray, rain, or mist. This salt-bearing moisture falls on plants that the elk consume, and thus they get all the salt they need.

Most elk hunters are familiar with the pellet-shaped droppings of an elk. Their quantity and freshness are good indications of the number and nearness of elk. The dry pellet form is seen in fall and winter and is primarily the result of a diet of dried grass and browse. Once some greenery is added to the diet in the spring, the form of the droppings begins to change. By June, when elk are eating a lot of fresh green forage, the droppings are soft, flat, elongated, or circular "chips" that resemble those of domestic cattle but are smaller.

An elk has thirty-four teeth in a full set. There are fourteen in the upper jaw—two canines, six premolars, and six molars—and twenty in the lower jaw—six incisors, two canines, six premolars and six molars. There are no incisors in the upper jaw. Elk crop food between the lower incisors and the hard dental pad in the upper gum.

The development and condition of an elk's teeth probably provide the most reliable evidence of the animal's age, up to about four years. After that, the wear and the staining of teeth suggest only in a general way whether the animals are prime adults, old adults, or senile adults.

Elk calves are born with the milk incisors showing, and within a week or so all the deciduous, or milk, teeth appear.* Within six months the first molar is usually present. In another twelve months the second molar grows in, as well as some permanent incisors and probably the canines By approximately two and one-half years of age, the elk has all its permanent teeth.

Like other ruminants, elk crop their food rapidly and swallow it quickly. When their appetites are satisfied, they retire to a less exposed spot to rest and ruminate, or chew their cuds. This ability to delay part of the eating process makes it unnecessary for relatively defenseless ruminants to stay on open feeding grounds while they chew their food.

Swallowed food goes into the first section of the elk's four-part stomach, the rumen. From this "storage compartment" small masses, or cuds, of food are regurgitated and chewed into a fine pulp.

I counted the number of chews by different elk and by the same elk on different cuds: the number varied between forty and fifty. It seems likely that the consistency of the food would determine the amount of chewing necessary. The soft green foods of early summer are certainly more easily pulverized than the dried grasses and browse foods of winter.

Chewed cuds go back into the rumen and, if thoroughly chewed and mixed with liquids, soon pass into the second compartment of the stomach, called the reticulum, and then, shortly, into the third section, the omasum. Here, water is absorbed, after which real digestion gets under way in the fourth stomach compartment, the abomasum or true glandular stomach.

The elk is a most adaptable animal. Its range many years ago included

---

*Most mammals are diphodont; i.e., they have two sets of teeth. The milk (first) teeth include only incisors, canines, and premolars. The permanent teeth, which come in following the milk teeth, consist of incisors, canines, premolars, and molars.—*The Editor.*

Georgia and the Carolinas, with their hot, humid climate, as well as Montana and Wyoming, with their subzero winters. Herds could also cope with extremes of moisture—from the Olympic Peninsula, where rainfall may reach 120 inches per year, to Arizona and New Mexico, where it may be about a tenth as much.

Today, elk live in heavily timbered areas and, except for a few minor variations, in mountainous country, to which they have apparently retreated in order to avoid the pressures of civilization. However, early records describing the great numbers of elk on the plains along with bison have led to speculation as to whether the elk was originally a plains animal or merely made migrations across the plains. It seems likely that before the coming of the white man, elk faced fewer dangers in open areas and therefore spent more time on the plains, where most of its food was to be found. But even in the plains states, elk utilized cover afforded by the wooded areas bordering rivers.

James H. Harper of the Oregon State Game Commission observed that most elk used open places for feeding but preferred to stay fairly close to standing timber for the safety it afforded. Mr. Harper's research was conducted in the great fir forest of the coastal range, where sections of virgin timber are bordered by logged-over areas. This seems to agree with findings about the habits of elk in other parts of the country: the animals prefer wooded tracts which offer protection from their enemies, especially man. Also, during the summer, forests provide cooling shade and some escape from insects. But timber alone isn't enough; it must be interspersed with ridges and clearings.

Timber harvesting has benefited elk to a considerable extent. Cut-over lands are soon covered with palatable nutritious forage plants that would not grow in the shade of dense stands of timber. Forest fires, although always tragic, are also followed by a growth of forage plants. During the winter, snow often forces elk to lower elevations, but only as a last resort: only a shortage of food will make them abandon the protective timber.

The ability of an elk to travel swiftly through broken and dense timber

36

Elk especially like open feeding areas that have protective cover nearby.

is truly remarkable. Despite the width of their antlers, even bull elk can make their way through thickets that are too dense for a man.

The name of this fine animal appears throughout the United States. Just in my home state, Oregon, there is an Elk Butte, an Elk City, three Elk Creeks, an Elk Flat, a pioneer post office called Elk Horn and another named Elkhead; also Elk Lake, Elk Mountain, Elk Point, Elk River, Elk Horn School, and Elkhorn Spring. In addition, the elk is depicted on the state seals of Idaho, Oregon, and Michigan.

Even bulls with very large antlers can move through thick timber with surprising ease and speed.

Spring

SPRING IS THE SEASON of triumph for elk. In northern ranges where severe weather has removed the unfit, survivors nibble greedily at the first green plants of spring as if anxious to get on with the business of the new year. Last year's bull calves move toward adult status with the appearance of velvet-covered head bumps that will eventually be their first antlers. Yearlings become two-year-olds, another year closer to maturity and their challenge for a place among the breeding bulls of the herd. Pregnant cows carrying the result of last autumn's matings seek isolation for the birthing of their calves. It is the beginning of a busy time.

Antler growth begins in the early spring, shortly after the previous year's antlers have been shed. Immature bulls and mature bulls in poor physical condition shed theirs later. One May 5 in Yellowstone National Park I counted six bulls still wearing the previous year's antlers.

Antler shedding, or casting, as it is also called, is apparently the result of glandular activity that weakens the junction of the antler and the pedicel, or protuberance on the elk's head from which the antlers grow. As the antler loosens, it can easily be knocked off if brushed against an object. It may even fall off as a result of a rapid head movement or jarring. I know of a spot near a fence that elk regularly jumped which had a liberal crop of shed antlers, indicating that the impact of landing was sufficient to dislodge the loosened antlers.

Antlers may be dropped one at a time or together. The loss of one or both antlers seems to confuse some of the bulls for a short time, probably

39

Springtime's first green offerings are welcome.

due to the sudden loss of weight from their heads. When an antler falls off, it leaves a shallow, rounded depression in the pedicel, which normally shows some bleeding. This soon scabs over and new growth begins. In April it will become noticeable as a rounded swelling of the tip of the pedicel. The "velvet" that covers the growing antler is actually an extension of the skin. Nourishment and mineral salts for the growing antlers are supplied from a network of fine blood vessels inside the antler, which is filled with soft bone tissue, and by the blood vessels in the velvet.

Because antlers grow from the base upward, the lower portions reach maximum size before growth of the points is complete. Mature antlers are pure bone, and the wall of the shaftlike antler is quite dense, while the interior is filled with spongy bone. Ossification begins at the base and keeps pace with the growing tip. At any point on the antler, the material below is harder than the material above. During the growth period, the tips have an elastic consistency, and the antlers feel warm to the touch because of the flow of blood in the velvet.

During this time bull elk are careful of their antlers. If they itch, the animals scratch delicately. An injury at this time causes the antlers to

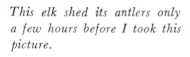
This elk shed its antlers only a few hours before I took this picture.

These velvet-covered "buds" will eventually become large antlers.

By June, both the brow and the bez tines are already showing.

grow in an abnormal manner. Some years ago an elk was seen in the Wichita National Wildlife Refuge in Oklahoma with three antlers. It was thought that this was the result of an injury to one antler during the early stages of its growth. The right antler was normal and had five points. One left antler was in normal position and had five points but lacked a brow tine. The second left antler was two inches in front of the other. It was well developed with four tines. The extra antler appeared to have come from the brow tine on the left side, which split off at an early age.

Damage to the pedicel, or an abnormal pedicel, creates abnormalities that will occur each time a new set is grown. Several tines may rise from a deformed pedicel; or there may be none at all. Antler growth at weird angles may also result.

Great variations in spring weather in different sections of elk range cause seasonally influenced herd activities to occur later in some areas than in others. Spring comes much earlier along the coast of northern California, Oregon, and Washington than it does in the high country of the Rocky Mountains. Several years ago, I spent a few days in March in Prairie Creek State Park in northwestern California and found the elk to be fat and healthy-looking. The weather was warm, and there was an abundance of food. A week later, I went to the National Elk Refuge in Jackson Hole, Wyoming, and saw a herd of six thousand elk that were just getting by on supplemental feedings of hay. Deep snow covered the surrounding mountains and hills, the elk's normal summer range. The day I left the refuge, it was snowing hard and six inches of new snow covered the valley floor.

This is more or less typical of the severe weather in high mountain ranges: it arrives early and stays late. The effect on elk is to produce some rather spectacular migrations. Little is known about the seasonal movements of early-day herds, but it seems likely that, with no white

43

A migrating elk herd seeks the sparse remains of last year's meadow grass under a thin blanket of fresh spring snow.

These elk are migrating to their high summer range as fast as the weather permits.

hunter and settler around, the animals had no need to retreat to the remote heights that some present-day herds inhabit. Nor would they have found it necessary to migrate over long distances. The elk that formerly inhabited the eastern and central United States had to contend with only minor variations in altitude between summer and winter ranges; consequently, little migratory movement was necessary.

In the Rocky Mountain regions of the West, however, deep snows force elk to seek new feeding grounds at lower elevations. While their spring migration routes are pretty much the reverse of fall migrations, there is a different motivation. In the fall, elk migrate to find food. But in the spring they leave the lower elevations, where new and plentiful forage comes early, to follow the snow line back into the mountains with a seeming eagerness that is not fully understood. It is believed that some elk actually force their way through deep snow to reach favorite areas. Of course, not all elk are in such a hurry to leave the valleys. Some may be found there at all seasons of the year.

The most impressive migrations occur in Yellowstone National Park and the Jackson Hole region. Many of these animals travel a distance equal to sixty airline miles between winter and summer ranges. Their return to summer ranges is influenced by the weather. A heavy and lingering snow pack or severe spring snow storms may make spring migration late in starting—or it may start and then be held up by bad weather. Much of the summer range in the northwestern Wyoming area is over 7,000 feet high. With winter snow hanging on until well into summer, elk may not arrive in this area until July.

Migration begins gradually and progresses slowly as the animals fan out and follow familiar trails. Elk are creatures of habit. They spend the winter in the same place year after year and follow the same routes back and forth. Calves learn from their mothers the first time and make their own way after that. Old elk trails are deeply worn into the ground.

Calves are generally born in late May and early June; however, tule

45

elk in California give birth about a month earlier. Some unusual birth dates have been reported. Several calves were born to captive elk cows in the Portland (Oregon) Zoo in July, and Ernest Thompson Seton reported finding an elk calf less than a week old on October 15. The latest reported birth I have found occurred on November 6. During long, late-starting migrations, pregnant cows generally stop to have their calves and then remain where they are, seldom moving more than a few hundred yards away from the youngsters until they are strong enough to travel, usually two or three weeks later. Meanwhile, the dry cows and bulls continue on their way. The new mothers and babies join another herd moving through the area.

Expectant cows do not seek out a favorite calving ground. Instead, when the gestation period of between 249 and 265 days draws to an end, she leaves the herd—usually a small one of fifteen to twenty—and finds a secluded area. If it is a herd whose migratory movements are insignificant or entirely absent, the rest of the elk remain in the vicinity. This is true of the Prairie Creek, California, herds, to which, normally, the cow returns—when her calf is strong enough to move about readily.

Single calves are the rule, but occasionally twins are born. A study of Yellowstone elk disclosed 2 cases of twinning in 896 pregnancies. Data for other herds revealed similar ratios, with 3 twins out of 794 pregnancies. Sex ratio of new calves is very close to 100:100.

Twin elk calves like these are rare.

Newborn calves weigh between 20 and 45 pounds—a rather wide variation—but the average weight is around 30 pounds. One observer reported that the cow gives birth while in a reclining position. I would judge this to be normal. The cow's activity immediately following birth undoubtedly depends on the difficulty of the birth and her physical condition, as well as that of the calf.

In his report, "Biology of the Elk Calf," Donald E. Johnson stated that nine out of twelve newborn calves were unable to walk and three of these were unable to stand. Those that could walk were very unstable. Day-old calves ran very unsteadily.

I was fortunate enough to be at the zoo in Portland, Oregon, one morning shortly after an elk calf was born. According to one of the caretakers, birth had occurred about fifteen minutes before I arrived and began making observations. The calf was lying on the ground, looking rather wet and bedraggled. Its eyes were open. The cow was standing over her calf, licking it clean.

I left for about ten minutes, and when I returned, the calf was trying to stand. After making a number of attempts in a period of several minutes, the youngster managed to get to its feet. As it stood tottering precariously on spraddled legs the cow started licking it again. This was too much for the calf's delicate balance, and it fell. In five minutes it had recovered sufficiently to try standing again. This time it managed with much less difficulty. It staggered a step or two and then was content just to stand. Twenty minutes later it had gained so much confidence that it began nosing around the forequarters of its mother, as if searching for her udder. The calf kept at its explorations and, after ten minutes or so, found what it was looking for. As best I could tell from where I was standing, the calf began nursing. This was not much more than one hour after its birth.

I then left the cow and calf, but returned two hours later to see what progress had been made. The baby was lying down about ten feet from where it had been born. It was dry, bright-eyed and healthy-looking.

*As the newborn elk makes its first attempts to stand,
the mother is busy cleaning it.*

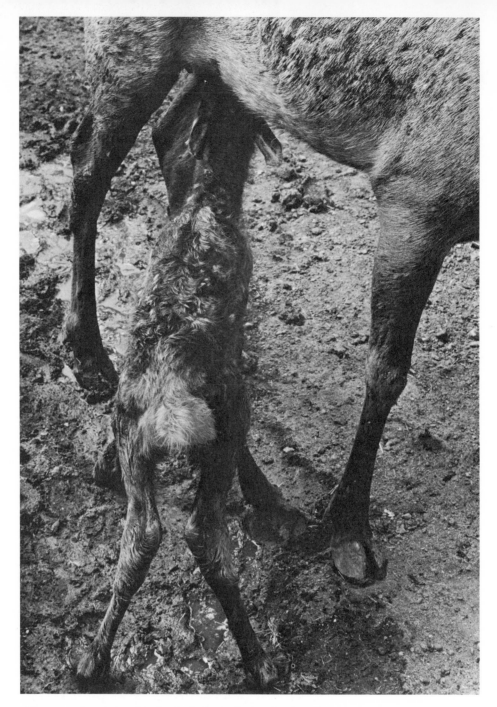

About one hour after birth, the baby feeds for the first time.

This day-old Roosevelt elk calf was hiding, and remained perfectly still even when I came quite close to photograph her.

I noticed that the other older elk, which had been out of the enclosure during the birth period, had been allowed to join mother and baby. They took no special notice of the baby, but the mother apparently thought they might represent a threat to her calf's welfare. She walked about twenty feet and nipped one of the other cows. The scene I left, however, was a peaceful one.

Elk calves vary considerably in color. Some have soft and indistinct white spots; the spots on others are brighter. But I have seen no elk calves with white spots as prominent as those of mule deer or white-tailed deer fawns. The only very young calves I have had an opportunity to study were Roosevelt elk, but descriptions given by others of Rocky Mountain elk calves conform to what I have seen. Tule elk calves are described as being light rufous in color and only faintly spotted.

A day-old Roosevelt calf I spent some time with in the coastal range of Oregon was basically light reddish-brown. It had darker brown hair on the neck and on the upper jaw from just below the eyes down to the nose. A dark brown streak approximately 1½ inches wide extended down the backbone from head to buff-colored rump patch. A row of white spots paralleled this dorsal streak on each side. Irregular spotting on the sides extended up over the shoulders and onto the neck. The tiny hoofs and nose were black.

For the first three or four days of its life, the calf is weak and un-

51

steady on its feet and spends most of its time in hiding, lying down beside big logs, under bushes, or at the base of large trees. This is something a calf does naturally. The cow does not choose a hiding place for the youngster, although Margaret Altmann reported that after the first nursing the calf either drops down to a resting position or is pushed down by the cow.

If no danger is present, the young elk lies relaxed and easy as it looks about with head raised. At the first sign of danger it flattens its head and neck on the ground and remains motionless.

While traveling through Oregon's timber-covered coastal range I photographed a calf estimated to be approximately a day old. I caught my first glimpse of it under a bush in a clearing a short distance from dense timber. Its head and neck were down flat on its forelegs, which were stretched out in front. I spent thirty minutes inching my way forward to close the fifteen-foot distance between us. When I got to within five feet, the youngster seemed almost ready to panic. Saliva dripped from its mouth—an indication, I suppose, of fright—but still it did not run. It did raise its head slowly, but it would not look directly at me. Easing the camera to within three feet of the calf, I took another picture. This was too much. It got up and staggered off, weak-kneed and wobbly.

During all this time I could hear the calf's mother "barking" her disapproval of my presence. She was not too far away but remained concealed in the heavy timber nearby. James A. Harper, who has caught and tagged several hundred elk calves in that same area, told me there seemed to be a definite correlation between the age of the calf and the degree of protection the cow was willing to provide. The older the calf, the more aggressive was the mother. He described an occasion when a calf probably not over one hour old had been caught and tagged. Apparently the new parent had not yet had time to fully develop motherly ties and she left the scene. After the calf was released, the tagging crew retired to an observation post some distance away

A mother identifies her elk calf by its odor.

but the cow never returned. They had to take the youngster home and raise it by hand.

On the other hand, Harper or one of his helpers is occasionally treed by an irate mother elk. The calves of these extremely protective cows are generally several days old. It seems that it takes a few days for a mother to form a strong attachment to her calf.

There are two schools of thought as to whether or not a newborn elk calf has any scent. Some contend that there is no odor; others believe that elk babies do have a scent, but not a strong one. According to one recorded report, a dog of a species with normally sensitive noses passed within five feet of an elk calf without picking up its scent. Coyotes have also been known to miss concealed elk calves. Other observations, however, show that a cow elk identifies her own calf by scent and rejects calves not her own. While I have made only casual observations of calves two and three weeks old, these observations indicate that calves have enough individual odor to identify them to other elk.

Like most wild youngsters, elk calves develop rapidly. By the time they are a week or ten days old they run rapidly and can scramble over logs three or four feet in diameter.

A mother with a new calf keeps last year's offspring at a distance.

When a calf is strong enough to travel, the cow brings it in to join a herd.

Spring

A cow's relationship to her previous year's offspring changes drastically after she gives birth to a new calf. Yearlings are tolerated only at a distance. If they approach too closely they are threatened or even struck by the cow with her forefeet. Usually, the blow does not land, as a yearling reacts quickly when the cow lays back her ears and comes at it with head up and forefoot raised. Rejected by their mothers, yearlings may gradually withdraw from the cows and band together in subgroups. Yearling males may form loose associations with groups of mature bulls.

One June I was on hand when a cow and her calf joined a herd. It was probably a reunion, since it was one of the Prairie Creek herds which don't really migrate. Arriving at the beach section of the park in early afternoon, I located a herd composed of cows, yearlings, two calves, and one young bull that was probably going into his third year. There were twenty animals in all.

The next afternoon when I visited the herd I counted three calves. Sometime during the morning a cow had brought her calf in to join the herd.

This newest addition was noticeably smaller than the other two calves and probably a week or two younger. The older elk showed no concern, but the two larger calves seemed quite interested in the new arrival as the three moved along with the herd in a small group of their own. Finally, one of the older calves advanced on the newcomer and made a threatening gesture with a front foot. The smaller calf retreated and thereby acknowledged the dominant status of the larger.

Later the same day I watched the two older calves indulge in an extended period of vigorous play. It was one of those beautifully sunny days with a minimum of wind that come all too infrequently to that section of the Pacific Coast. It was warm enough to be comfortable and cool enough to be invigorating, at least for me. I don't know whether or not the elk felt the same way, but something certainly started the youngsters off.

55

Elk calves at play.

As the group moved slowly up the beach, the older ones stopped occasionally to nibble a clump of grass or sample other appetizing plants. The calves followed along, and every few minutes one or the other of the older ones would run a few steps, dodging, jumping about, and leaping into the air. This exuberant display looked as if it might be a preliminary to some interesting action. I hastily dug out a 640-mm. telephoto lens and mounted it on the camera. The herd was about a hundred yards away, and I didn't want to risk moving closer and disturbing them. This 12+ power telephoto would, in effect, give me the same picture I would get with a normal lens at around twenty-five feet.

Finally the two playful youngsters met head to head. There was a moment's hesitation and then both raised up on their hind legs and struck at each other with their forefeet. This was just play-fighting, however, and there was no real attempt to strike one another. They sparred in this manner for a minute or so, continuing to jump and dodge about a lot. As with youngsters everywhere, I suppose, one of

This cow elk is "baby-sitting" while the other mothers are off feeding or resting.

the two proved stronger. Then the game changed to something like tag, with the dominant calf chasing the other around and around. A cow walked by, possibly the mother of one of the participants, but she showed no awareness of the playful calves, nor they of her.

Playfulness is not confined to young calves. The warm days of early spring, especially after a hard winter, sometimes cause the nine-month-old calves to scamper about and kick up their heels as if in anticipation of easier times to come. Even though they look somewhat emaciated and may be weak from living on short rations, spring is in the air and they respond to it.

Once back in a herd, a cow seems to relax her protective activities and allows the calf a great deal of freedom. While the adults are feeding, youngsters move about freely, sometimes at quite a distance from the older ones. They lie down wherever the notion strikes them, and during their first few weeks they rest frequently.

Cow elk have a cooperative "baby-sitting" arrangement for the protection of their calves. It is not clear how it is made or which of the

57

cows takes over the duty, but one or two mothers stay with the young while the others are off feeding. I once spent some time watching such a group, which consisted of three calves and a cow that was the mother of one of the calves. The youngsters spent most of the time bedded down on a grassy slope about five to ten feet apart. One got up once to inspect another, but otherwise they seemed quite independent of each other.

Margaret Altmann reported seeing as many as seventy calves in the "elk-calf pools" in Jackson Hole country. The attentiveness of the baby-sitter decreases as the youngsters increase their feeding on plants, so that by September this protectiveness is no longer necessary and the calves feed with the herd.

James A. Harper reported that cows were observed calling their calves away from the baby-sitter for a nursing period, even if they were as much as a hundred yards from the calves. Influenced probably by

This nursing calf is about three weeks old.

Since a cow usually allows only her own calf to nurse, the hungry youngster at left can only watch and wait for its mother to appear.

the discomfort of a too-full udder, a cow would stop feeding, look in the direction of the calves, and emit a high-pitched neigh. Her calf, which obviously recognized the call, would stop whatever it was doing and listen. Sometimes it took several neighs for the calf to locate the source. If the cow was hidden by trees or shrubs or was in a gully, the calf would just stand and listen. When the cow finally moved into view the calf would run over and start nursing. In a typical gesture the baby would butt the cow vigorously to keep the milk flowing.

In the beginning, calves nurse five or six times during the day. The nursing periods last from a half-minute to almost two minutes. I have found no reports of observed night-nursing sessions, but they may occur, particularly when the calf is quite young and feeds often because of its limited capacity.

I saw a resting cow get up from her bed and walk ten feet to where her calf was lying. She touched it with her nose. The young one got up immediately and started nursing. After thirty seconds, the cow terminated the nursing session by walking off. The calf hesitated a moment, as if it wanted to continue feeding, and then returned to the spot where it had previously bedded. After giving the place a sniff as if to identify it, the youngster lay down again.

59

In general, nursing periods are ended in this manner. Additional attempts by the calf to nurse are similarly rejected. If a calf is persistent, the cow may strike it across the back with a front hoof or butt it in the side. This rebuff is sufficient to discourage the calf and send it back to the babysitter.

Only on extremely rare occasions does a cow elk permit a calf other than her own to nurse. One amusing report told of a calf that slipped in from the rear to join a cow's own calf in nursing; the trespasser escaped detection for almost half a minute. James A. Harper reported that he also watched several calves nurse a single cow and that this occurred several times. He also described seeing one calf go from one cow to another, nursing for short periods at each, and told how two calves nursed one cow and then both changed to a second cow. Thus, it would appear that some cows do not mind which calves they nurse. It would also appear that some calves have bigger appetites than others!

Young calves nurse in a standing position, but as they grow larger they may have to kneel to reach the udder. This seems to be the most common position after they are two to two and a half months old. Calves have been observed nursing while the cows are lying down. To accomplish this the calf forces its head under the cow's rear leg. Some mothers lift their legs to make it easier for the calf to reach their udders.

Soon after the cow and her new calf join the herd, the youngster begins to emulate the older animals and to nibble at plants. At first it does this mostly out of curiosity, but within a month or so it is feeding fairly extensively on grass and browse. By the time it is two or three months old it grazes regularly with the adults. Weaning is generally complete by early October, although some calves can be seen still obtaining milk from their mothers in January. A late-December examination of forty-six female elk over two years old disclosed that twenty were still lactating. This would indicate that a high percentage of calves were still nursing.

Yearlings have been observed nursing, and only a few years ago I

This nine-month-old calf, standing by its mother, now weighs about 250 pounds.

photographed a yearling female nursing in late June. Despite the fact that she was almost as large as the cow, she nursed standing up. This was the same cow, I think, that earlier in the day had bluffed a couple of charges at me when she apparently thought I was getting too close. Her protectiveness, and the fact that she was giving milk at this time of the year and had allowed a yearling to nurse, indicated that she had probably had a calf and lost it in some manner. A spikehorn with antlers a foot long was seen nursing in the middle of August. As might be imagined, he was having great difficulty.

Although calves may continue to rely upon their mothers' milk well into the fall, they become independent of this food source much earlier. The point at which an elk calf can subsist on plants alone varies, but as a general rule a two-month-old calf could get along without its mother's milk.

There are, of course, always some losses among calves only a few days old. The available data do not suggest that the number is dispro-

A cow herd at rest.

portionate. Most of these are probably calves born of a cow that was undernourished during pregnancy. Severe winter weather undoubtedly has a bad effect on the newborn calves, especially in northern Rocky Mountain ranges, where early June snowstorms are not uncommon. Nevertheless, a substantial percentage of young calves are lost from causes unknown.

At first elk calves gain from one to two pounds a day, but their rapid growth rate generally slows down during fall and winter when food becomes scarce. A two-month-old calf weighs between 90 and 130 pounds; at nine months, about 280 pounds; and at twenty-one months, 450 pounds or so.

The American elk is essentially a herd animal. Herding is an adaptation providing protection from predators in open country, and an indication that elk formerly spent more time in the open than does the present population. During the early spring in northern ranges, where the weather continues its wintry ways, the animals can be found in herds of several hundred; in Jackson Hole, several thousand. These large herds come together in the winter and contain both sexes and all age groups. In late spring, herds of cows separate from herds of bulls. The cow herds are made up of family groups and contain old and young cows and yearling bulls. Later, as the new calves develop, they become a part of the cow herd, which stays together through the summer.

A typical cow herd consists of from ten to twenty-five animals. Its structure seems to be based on family relationship, and the members may represent three or four generations. James A. Harper stated that there is a continuous interchange between herds of Roosevelt elk, even during the calving season. This would help to prevent inbreeding.

William Graf, from his studies of Roosevelt elk, noted that two herds he had observed closely had similar membership: one yearling and one two-year-old bull, five calves in one herd and four in the other, four

Roosevelt elk.

or five cows of breeding age, and apparently about the same number of cows that had not reached breeding age.

The social organization of the herd is matriarchal: the leader is a mature cow, usually the oldest cow in the herd. She is the undisputed leader and is always in front when the herd moves along the trails. Jim Yoakum, wildlife specialist of the Bureau of Land Management, described to me an example of this leadership which took place when a herd of California Roosevelt elk was about to cross a highway. The herd approached the road and then stopped until the leader decided to cross. She went first; the others followed.

The matriarch makes decisions about crossing streams, walking narrow trails, or escaping from apparent danger.

Although elk herds exist as social groups, individuals both within families and outside them keep definite distances apart. In maintaining these separations, hierarchical relationships between the elk become evident. Mature cows are dominant over young cows, young bulls with spike horns, and two-year-old bulls. Spike bulls are dominant over yearling cows. Adult bulls are dominant over cows and younger bulls. Calves, of course, are at the bottom of the dominance structure, but, in the cow herds I have studied, the older animals usually let the calves do whatever they wished. The calves may be casually pushed aside if they are in the way of an older animal, but for the most part this is done without rancor.

Dominant status within a herd is maintained by a show of aggression, in which the individual elk advances toward another with ears back, nostrils flared, and teeth bared. The threat alone generally sends a younger elk scurrying away. If the victim doesn't scare easily, it may be bitten or struck with a forefoot. If dominance has not been definitely established, the opponents may face each other in aggressive attitudes. If neither retreats they may rear up on their hind legs and flail away at each other with their front feet, like a couple of incompetent boxers. Usually little harm comes from this, as the few connecting

This bull, its five-point antlers still in velvet, raised its head and shook it from side to side to express annoyance at my presence.

blows strike the forelegs. The first one to drop its forefeet to the ground is the loser.

Active aggression occurs most frequently when the cows are close together, as they are during the peak of the rutting season, when the bulls keep the animals bunched. This "boxing" is seen often between cows in the massed winter herds on the National Elk Refuge in Jackson Hole, when from six to eleven thousand elk are in the valley.

Bulls also fight with their forefeet when their antlers are still in velvet and are not yet suitable weapons.

67

A calf also looked put out as it inspected me.

The cow herd is guarded by one or more mature cows, which probably achieve this position of responsibility simply because they are older and more aware of potential danger. When something interrupts their normal activity, they look steadily at the disturbing object and may "bark" tentatively. If it is a false alarm, the guards resume whatever they were doing and the whole herd relaxes. If the danger seems real, they may sniff the wind while walking away with a measured, stiff-legged gait, but they are ready to run should it become necessary to do so. The leader decides when it is time to move. Elk do not always run

The cow moving away on the left is apparently the leader. The other elk will soon follow her.

directly away from a disturbance, as is the habit of sheep, cattle, bison, and horses. They may go toward it and break past.

In areas where winter weather is not a problem, bull herds exist at all seasons except during the rut. Even where winters are severe, bulls tend to maintain their herds as long as possible. Near Mammoth Hot Springs in Yellowstone National Park one February I checked a herd of six great bulls each morning for a week. I always found them at dawn feeding on the wind-swept slopes of a treeless butte where the rising winter sun edged their magnificent antlers with frosty gold. I got too close to them one morning, and they trotted off through belly-deep snow to reach the shelter of a grove of leafless aspen a quarter of a mile away.

Bull herds may contain spike bulls and two-year-olds, but the members are mostly three years old or older. Spikes generally stay with the cow herds; two-year-olds come and go. The social organization of a bull herd is not very strong. Members may wander off, and any one of them can start a flight from danger. When this happens, the animals, following no leader, may go in many different directions.

The bull herd breaks up with the rutting season, when they join the cows and drive off the spike bulls. Instead of bull herds there are now separate groups of bachelors, immature bulls, and herd masters.

This young bull looks trim and sleek in his shiny summer coat.

Summer

An ELK has little to bother it in summer except heat and insects. Food is plentiful; enemies are few and scarce. Calves are strong and able to travel with the herd. There is little to do but eat, rest, and grow. The animals, trim and glossy in their rich reddish-brown summer coats, seem to enjoy it. The season's extended daylight hours provide a lot of time for just loafing in some favorite spot.

Two months earlier, during the spring molt, the elk looked ragged and worn. Long, drab, and lifeless winter hair had hung in unsightly patches. The oldest animals had shed first, the youngest last. In May the new hair was noticeable especially about the head and the legs. Finally, by June or soon afterward, when all the old hair is gone, the elk emerge resplendent in close-fitting coats of short, stiff hairs. This thin summer pelage shows off their superb physical structure admirably, for the now-bountiful grasses and browse have filled out the body hollows caused by winter's short rations.

The elk's winter coat starts growing as soon as the summer one is completed. Obvious winter pelage growth has been noted as early as July 23, and by the middle of August nearly all elk show signs of a grayish winter coat. This grows denser and heavier through autumn, reaching full growth in early winter. The length of the hair ranges from 2 inches on the sides and belly to 5 inches on the neck and shoulders.

The winter pelage includes a woolly undercoat beneath cervine guard

73

hairs which give the elk its characteristic color. This would appear to be a most efficient covering, and elk seem unaffected by extreme cold unless they are sick. I have frequently watched elk during intensive cold periods when there was a lot of deep snow, and as far as I could tell, they did not look for shelter or otherwise indicate any concern. On the other hand, they are annoyed by heat and try to escape it. Even as early as March and April some elk indicate their discomfort by bedding down in snowdrifts.

Tule elk, however, are an exception in their response to temperatures. In their former range in California, and to some extent in their present range, extreme cold and even long periods of moderate cold are unknown. Hot weather is more the rule. The strenuous activities of the tule elk rut take place when summer temperatures are often over 100 degrees Fahrenheit; this apparently causes little discomfort.

Tule elk calves also grow a winter coat that looks about the same as that of the older ones. During the summer the white spots fade, and by the middle of August or early September they have disappeared.

During the summer, ponds and the shallows of lakes are favorite spots for elk: they enjoy playing in the water as much as they enjoy drinking it, for they can cool off and get rid of insects. Calves and even some of the older animals like to run through the shallows, kicking and splashing. Cows have been seen standing in a foot or so of water splashing with their feet for several minutes at a time. They obviously make the most of summer bathing opportunities.

Elk are also good swimmers and readily cross rivers. One of the Roosevelt elk introduced on Afognak Island in Alaska swam through the cold salt water to another island a mile away. A four-day-old calf swam across a sixty-foot-wide, four-foot-deep stream to join its mother on the opposite side after it had been handled by a tagging team.

Another form of elk "play" in which both adult cows and adult bulls engage has been reported. This involves picking up objects with the

75

A rare sight: elk cows at play with their calves.

Elk are good swimmers and enjoy being in the water in summer.

Elk calves play with sticks by picking them up and tossing them down. Adults seem to like this game too.

mouth, lifting them high, and dropping them. I have not seen adult elk do this, but I did see a month-old calf pick up a foot-long stick and juggle it around in its mouth for several minutes before dropping it. His feisty actions reminded me of a smart-aleck child imitating a grownup.

Some time in July or early August the antlers reach maximum growth. Once ossification is complete and the antlers are strong and solid, the velvet covering no longer serves its purpose and begins to dry up. Apparently this results in an itching sensation, and the bulls rub their antlers against brush and trees. Since the velvet is not completely dead at this time, rubbing causes some inconsequential bleeding, and at times strips may hang down from the antlers like pieces of torn cloth. Eventually it is all rubbed off, at least on mature, healthy animals. Imma-

By July, a bull's antlers are well developed and show their final form.

ture or diseased elk lose the velvet later or sometimes not at all. Continued rubbing of the antlers against trees and brush gives them a high polish and the vegetable stains change them from their normal white to a beautiful brown. I once tried scrubbing a section of elk antler to remove this color, but strong soap and a stiff brush didn't do a thing to it.

Normally, elk rest at night and are active during the daylight hours. They spend midmorning to midafternoon ruminating and resting, although elk with larger appetites than the others continue to feed sporadically. An intensive feeding period starts around 4 P.M. and lasts until dark. As the days become shorter and food is not so plentiful, elk feed and travel during the day and continue to do most of their resting at night.

Studies of the Roosevelt elk in Oregon's coastal range produced a definite pattern in the feeding habits of elk. Although winter observations were not included in the study, it is reasonable to assume that herd actions then would be similar as long as weather conditions permitted. The observations indicated that the elk feed over one area for one to three days and then move on, not returning for two or three weeks. This seems to be the rule regardless of the type of country (mountainous, hilly, or flat) and the plants that grow there. As herds move about their home ranges, they sometimes meet and join herds from adjoining ranges. As many as six small bands may merge for periods that range from a few hours to several days. When such a combined herd does break up, there may be some interchange of herd animals.

In their movements about their home territories, elk demonstrate a marked tendency to use trails consistently. These well-worn paths throughout the range indicate that elk follow routes requiring the least expenditure of energy. For example, they traverse a hillside instead of

The herd finds all it needs to eat in knee-deep grass.

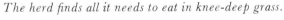

79

making steep up-and-down climbs, the way deer do. Elk show little inclination to avoid swamps during normal travel, but when threatened they try to stay on more solid ground. They seem to dislike small ravines covered with dense brush, but there are usually elk trails in larger canyons that contain flowing water and a clearing now and then. These paths generally run fairly close to the sides of the stream.

Variations in daily routines occur as a result of wind, rain, or other changes in the weather. On warm, calm days elk feed steadily, moving only enough to reach the next forage plant. When the temperature is high and the humidity low, the animals retreat into the timber until it gets cooler toward evening. On rainy or cool days with high humidity, elk are active all day and spend little time in the timber. When barometric pressure falls, elk become restless and nervous and feed in haphazard fashion, often going over the same spot several times. Bedding periods are short, and seldom will all members of a herd be bedded down at the same time. High winds cause the animals to seek shelter in timbered ravines, but if the wind is strong enough to break off branches, the elk prefer to find a clearing on the lee side of a hill or ridge.

After feeding, it's time for a nap in the warm sun.

John E. Schwartz reported that, during the summer, elk in the Olympics can be found bedded down on open river bars during the middle of the day, apparently to take advantage of air currents that help ward off flies.

An elk bed is where the animal spends its resting hours. However, elk seem to seek bedding grounds that are close to food. Elk have chosen these grounds on the tops of ridges, on the sides of canyons, in the bottoms of ravines, in open meadows, and in small timber clearings. Choice of location is undoubtedly influenced by potential danger, and for this reason a high point is frequently sought out. The resting animal not only has a good view of the neighborhood; it also is able to take advantage of any rising air currents that might carry scent upward. In addition, a high point often provides safe avenues for retreat. Preference has been shown for spots near the base of a large tree or stump, or under an overhanging log. Litter-free ground is preferred. Most elk, especially cows, rest and sleep with the head held erect. Bulls with large antlers sometimes rest their heads on the ground, probably to relieve the weight of their heavy antlers.

It appears that an individual animal has no special attachment to a particular bed, although the herd may repeatedly use the same bedding grounds. At times it seems that the animals just lie down wherever they happen to be.

Sometimes a dominant animal takes over the bed of a subordinate. The subordinate may, in turn, take over from another elk that it dominates.

At the conclusion of a resting period, elk usually yawn and stretch, but I have seen them stand up in their beds and immediately start feeding. I watched a herd of twenty animals one afternoon as it terminated the rest period. The first to rise looked like a yearling cow. She walked slowly away and started feeding a hundred yards from the herd. About every thirty seconds after that, another elk got up and joined the feeding group. In about ten minutes all were up and busy cropping grass.

81

When a bull decides to lie down, he sinks slowly down as far as he can. Then he relaxes and drops suddenly to the ground, landing with a force that rocks his head back.

Scratching elk sometimes look like contortionists.

Antlers are good for scratching an otherwise hard-to-reach itch.

A certain amount of restlessness is always evident in a bedded herd as one or another animal scratches, stretches, or changes position. Seldom does an elk remain asleep or motionless for more than thirty minutes at a time. Usually there is at least one wide-awake elk acting as sentinel. Even while asleep, an elk is sensitive to sounds: a suspicious noise brings its ears to attention even though its eyes may remain closed. If nothing further happens, the elk relaxes its ears; if the danger becomes real, the animal awakens, rises, and takes whatever protective action is required.

Elk spend a surprising amount of time scratching and grooming themselves. Grooming consists mostly of licking and chewing at all accessible parts of the body; at the same time the animal is usually scratching its head and neck with its hind foot. The scratching is apt to be directed at parasites. On occasion elk help the grooming process along by licking and biting one another.

Another interesting and unusual form of behavior among Roosevelt elk, called "sign-post" activity, has been described in detail by William

Graf. James A. Harper also described this phenomenon. I have not seen it, nor have I found any records of similar observations involving other elk subspecies. Basically, the elk shave bark from trees with their lower incisors and then rub their heads and parts of their bodies on the shaved parts of the tree. Cow elk have been seen so occupied most often, but Graf described actions of a herd bull which scraped an alder sapling with his antlers during the rutting season. Harper mentioned a spike-horn similarly occupied.

While these actions can take place almost anywhere, elk "sign-posting" is found most often around loafing and resting spots. There seems to be no favored kind of tree. Prior to actually scraping, the animal carefully draws its muzzle up and down over the trunk. Presumably, it is smelling the area thoroughly and may do so for as long as five seconds. When it draws its incisors across the trunk, thin ribbons of bark, usually about an eighth of an inch wide, drop to the ground. After several scrapes the animal rubs its muzzle, face, or head on the newly exposed part of the tree. This may be followed by rubbing the head against its own flanks. This rubbing action is more deliberate and massage-like than the scratching an elk does to relieve an itch.

So far no one has advanced a completely acceptable explanation for this behavior. There is no noticeable odor for either the scraped parts of the tree or its juices which might act as insect repellent. Graf suggests that tree-rubbing serves to mark the territory occupied by a herd. However, there doesn't seem to be much reason for territorial proclamations since elk are not antagonistic about encroachments by other elk.

While cow herds are taking it easy on the lush summer range, bachelor groups of mature bulls can be found in the same neighborhood. They may even be grazing near groups of cows, but for the most part they remain aloof. A bull herd is not as cohesively organized as a cow herd and is more like a gathering of independents that act as if they are not quite sure why they have assembled.

Summer

Any bull, even the youngest, may lead the group, if by "lead" we mean travel in front. There are no guards, as with the cow herds, but, when threatened, bulls show much less hesitancy about running away. They also demonstrate some playfulness by bucking, kicking, and butting each other. Some bugling takes place, even though it is summer and antlers are velvet-covered. This is sometimes followed by threatening gestures around other bulls, but these are only rehearsals for the serious business that will shortly follow when the rutting season begins.

A small bull herd.

Autumn

It was September 22, the first day of autumn. I was sitting in my parked car just off the road at Norris Junction in Yellowstone National Park. A pocket of dense fog hugged the ground. Evergreen trees ten feet away were barely identifiable shadows in the early-morning gloom. East of me, hidden by the fog, lay a large meadow. Somewhere in the meadow a bull elk bugled. This is one of the truly wild sounds to be heard in North America and, to me, rates with the howling of a coyote and the thrilling chorus of high-flying Canada geese as one of nature's grandest sounds.

My purpose in being at Norris Junction that particular morning was to get pictures of a bull elk bugling. Along with all my necessary camera equipment, I had some fog I definitely did *not* need. Half convinced I was wasting my time, I waited for the sun to burn off the misty cover. A brilliant white circle of sun showed briefly through a thin spot in the swirling fog, giving me momentary encouragement. At frequent intervals the elk's bugling broke the silence. Was it my imagination or did it sound closer . . . ?

Suddenly, out of the mist, the elk came striding toward me, a dark, soft-edged silhouette. Ten feet away he stopped, an enormous animal that looked large enough to walk right over me, car and all—an illusion that must have been a product of the fog and my overactive imagination. The mighty bull stretched his neck and bugled. Coming as it did right in my face, it seemed to shake the car. An involuntary shiver

89

ran down my back that was not entirely due to the chill morning air.

The bugle of a bull elk is a fascinating sound, but not at all what one might expect. The size of the animal and his great antlers suggest a deep bass: a more "manly" sound is in order, something akin to the bellowing of a domestic bull. And, as a matter of fact, bull elk have occasionally been heard giving a hoarse bellow. "Bugling" is not an especially good word to describe that combination bellow-whistle-grunt. It begins on a low, stirring, clear note, rises gradually to a high pitch, and ends in a shrill scream, followed by a series of grunts. It has been represented in this manner: "A-a-a-a-ai-e-eeeeeeeee! e-uh! e-uh! e-uh!"

The high notes are the ones most often heard, because bugling bulls are generally some distance away. But on this particular morning I heard it all! And I thought I could even smell the animal's strong, musty breath.

The bull went around the car, crossed the road, and disappeared in the fog, continuing to bugle every few minutes. And then I heard the distant call of another bull somewhere to the west. It was apparently this call that was antagonizing the first bull. Gradually, the bugling grew faint.

Little by little, the fog yielded to the morning sun, as if reluctant to let the warm rays drink up the dew that lay glistening on the yellow-brown grass. When the last wispy remnants of fog vanished, I could see that the meadow was empty and still.

It had been an altogether disappointing morning. As I was pondering what to do next I realized that the bugling no longer sounded so faint. In fact, it was growing louder! I quickly rolled down the car window and readied the camera.

As if on cue, the bull walked out of the timber and paused on a little mound about fifty feet away. He stretched out his neck and bugled. I took his picture.

Then he walked by and out into the center of the meadow. He grabbed a mouthful of meadow grass, thrashed about with his antlers,

Just before he stepped out of the stream, the mighty bull stretched his neck and bugled again.

and bugled again. I felt there was a desperate, frustrated quality to his restless calling, but this may have been my own invention. It was obvious, however, that he wanted a harem.

This big, handsome, mature bull with an effective-looking set of six-point antlers was what is known as a royal stag. But not royal enough to capture a harem, it would seem! Possibly his body strength was not up to the promise of his antlers.

I ruled out trying to get closer to him while he was in that open meadow—he might decide to take out his frustrations on me. North of the clearing came a distant bugling: a clue, perhaps, to the direction the bull would take when he left the meadow. I grabbed a telephoto-equipped camera and eased myself out of the car. I doubt that trying to hide was necessary, for the bull was certainly not interested in adding me to his nonexistent harem or concerned about me as a threat either to his safety or his love life, but I decided to take no chances. I backed away and made a long, concealed walk around to the north side.

There was a place at the edge of the meadow on a bit of high ground where I could be partially concealed and protected by a screen of trees. Just as I got into position the bull walked out onto the bank of the Gibbon River, which twists its way along the northern edge of the meadow. He bugled, stepped into the stream, and sounded his call again. Then he drank, bugled, and drank again. Finally, he moved on up the hill and disappeared into the timber, after stopping half in and half out of the water to bugle once more.

Because bugling is most often heard during the rutting season and one bull's call may be answered by another, it has been generally thought that this sound represents a challenge to other bulls. But bugling begins before the rutting season, while the bulls are still together and no threat is intended. Later, when rutting is at its peak, a bull bugles loudly and often, even when there are no other males around. Unattached bulls, such as the one just described, bugle often, but not apparently as a challenge. Bugling may be mostly a way to relieve the tension of pent-up emotion. There seems to be no record of one bull being frightened away by the bugling of another.

Bugling, although not confined to male elk or to any particular season, is most often done by bulls during the rut. Cow's bugling, heard usually in late spring, is not the loud, full-blown call of the rutting male. Young bulls are not known to bugle extensively. A spike-horn was seen bugling three times in early April in a high-pitched, reedy voice; and a two-year-old was heard in early December.

Bugling is the best known of all elk sounds, but it is by no means the only one they make. Most of the "talking" is between cows and calves, especially after they have joined the cow herds in early summer. It starts, however, before that. The calf squeals in a high-pitched, piercing tone when disturbed or alarmed. When badly frightened, such as when being captured by man, it squeals; the sound turns into a long-drawn-out scream which usually brings the cow on the run. Squealing occurs most often when the calf is separated from its mother at feeding time. By the strength, duration, and intensity of its calls, it expresses the urgency of the situation. The cow may reply with a high-pitched neigh, which is the same sound it uses to locate its offspring while the herd is feeding in timber or to call it when it is time to nurse. This sound is substantially the same as the squeal of the calf, only stronger and more mature. As the calf gets older it uses the same sounds it did at a younger age, but they become deeper in tone.

When alarmed or frightened, or even suspicious, older elk emit a call which is generally described as a bark. While this is a fairly accurate description, it can also be called a sharp, explosive snort. Both sexes use this call, but cows are most often heard making it.

James A. Harper and his co-authors, in their studies of Roosevelt elk in California, reported that, before the cow and the calf returned to the herd after the calf was born, this bark would cause the newborn calf to drop to the ground and conceal itself in whatever vegetation was available by stretching out and placing its head on the ground.

Once in the herd, the calf, hearing a bark, would look for the disturbance rather than hide automatically.

A bark also warns other members of the herd, although Olaus J. Murie believed that there is no conscious desire on the part of the elk to convey the idea to others. Harper's observations may indicate that the warning bark is directed toward the calf and the others benefit from it. On the other hand, since barking is not confined to cows with calves, it may be that this is a reflex response to threats and the unknown and that other elk, including calves, sense the warning involved.

A bark merely alerts an elk or a herd to the fact that there is possible danger nearby. Flight comes only after alerted animals have decided the danger is real.

Other minor sounds have been noted, but for the most part they do not seem to be made in order to communicate. But the upshot is that other elk can establish the location of any elk making these sounds.

In any event, elk seem to be about the noisiest of all our deer. In herds of from sixty to two hundred in the Jackson Hole summer ranges, there may be so much squealing, barking, roaring, and bugling when the herds are moving that they can be heard a mile away.

In late September several years ago I was photographing elk in Yellowstone National Park and for several days had been more or less following a big bull and his harem near Apollinaris Spring. I was on hand at daylight each morning and usually found them feeding in some meadow.

On one particular morning a hundred-yard-wide strip of timber separated the road from the meadow in which they were feeding. It had snowed a little the previous evening, but by dawn this had changed to a cold drizzle and only a few traces of snow were left in protected spots. The ground underfoot was soft, silent, and wet as I made my way slowly through the woods toward the feeding elk. As usual with this

94

My appearance did not alarm this feeding bull and his harem.

kind of park animal, I made no attempt at a hidden stalk. I preferred
to be seen rather than surprise them by suddenly appearing at a close
range. My movement through the timber produced only an occasional
disinterested glance from one of the cows. At the edge of the woods I
paused and looked around for the harem master. He was just disap-
pearing into timber on the other side in hot pursuit of another bull
that had apparently been trying a bit of cow stealing.

The harem was small: three cows, a couple of yearling females, and
two calves. After some fifteen minutes the bull had not returned, but
the females moved slowly toward me and entered the woods, feeding as
they came. In a few moments I was in the center of the loosely gathered
cows, spread out about a hundred feet. For the next half-hour I was a
part of the harem and moved slowly along with them as they fed.
Occasionally one would look at me casually, wondering, I suppose,
why I wasn't eating. They were nibbling at everything in sight like
hungry Swedes at a smörgasbord. One yearling took several bites of a
gray-green moss hanging from the trees. Another sampled the dead
brown stems of tall weeds. Normally, these would have been dry and
tough, but the rain had softened them until they could be easily eaten.
At any rate, the young elk seemed to like them. They all concentrated
on grass, but obviously relished tidbits of something different at frequent intervals.

Preliminaries to the active rutting season begin during the latter part
of August. Yearling spike bulls feeling sexual stimulation for the first
time disrupt the herd routines by "driving," "tending," and mounting
elk cows and by much mock fighting or sparring among themselves. No
actual matings take place, as the cows are not yet in heat. Such actions
by the young bulls may go on for as long as three weeks, but finally the
great herd bulls put in their appearance and take over. The exuberant
spikes are driven away by the harem bull. While it has been generally
believed that a bull "collects" a harem of cows, Margaret Altmann, in

This cow must have been hungry, for she sampled everything in sight—from grasses and thorny plants to tall dried weeds.

A bull places his chin on a cow's back to see if she is ready to breed.

her Wyoming studies, observed that an elk bull merely takes over a group of cows along with its calves, yearling cows, and young bulls. The young bulls are generally chased away and form bands of their own.

It also seems likely that some cows are gathered from unrelated herds to form a harem, since unattached bulls are constantly attempting to steal cows from established harems and surely, part of the time, succeed. When a bull takes on an unusually large herd of cows, it is almost impossible to keep them under sufficient control to avoid losing a few to "poaching" bachelors.

During the latter part of August older bulls begin to show signs of restlessness by belaboring trees and shrubs with their antlers a great deal. For a few days after they move in with the cow herds, several mature bulls may be fairly close to each other without any conflict. This situation does not last long, and by early September the harems have been formed. They may be of different sizes. A strong and energetic herd master can keep a group of thirty or so under control, but generally the number is less. Five to fifteen cows of breeding age usually compose a harem, but with the calves and yearlings included, it becomes a fairly large group.

These young bulls are only sparring. Later they will fight in earnest for the right to form a harem and breed.

For a few days the harem master has all he can do to keep the group together. Young bulls that have been ousted are trying to get back in, while their mothers, equally unhappy about the separation, are trying to get out to be near them. In addition, nearby bachelors always eager to run off with a cow present a constant threat.

After about a week, members of the harem learn that the herd bull intends to keep them, and they more or less resign themselves to staying with the group. The bull prefers to keep them in a clearing so that they can be under constant observation. If a cow does stray away, the bull charges after her and with a threatening upward sweep of his antlers brings her back. If the cow is slow to react she may get a not-too-gentle reminder from the bull's great antlers to hurry up. Usually the cows move too quickly to be struck. These herding tactics keep the harem together.

99

A bull and his harem.

The onset of the rutting season finds the mature bull elk in superb physical condition. Physiological development during the rut has resulted in a swollen neck, which makes the well-muscled harem masters seem even more massive than usual. As the season reaches its peak around the fourth week in September, harem masters reach a state of constant emotional stress. Their intense sexual urge drives them continuously. They eat very little and expend great amounts of energy.

A harem bull gives vent to his emotions in several ways. The most violent and noisy is his attack on trees, saplings, and other vegetation. With his great antlers he slashes and gouges with such force that shrubs and small trees are literally beaten to pieces. On one occasion a bull was so savage in his attack that he broke a red alder sapling more than two inches in diameter, an indication of the strength of the animal and the durability of his antlers. On occasion antlers have been broken by such actions.

During these violent bouts with trees and bushes, the bull eliminates copious amounts of urine that thoroughly soak the belly hair as well as the hair on the throat and the sides of his face. He may culminate his efforts by digging his antlers into the urine-soaked grass and tossing the material onto his back. He may then lie down and roll several times. A bull often completes an episode of this nature with a tangle of grass and vines caught in his antlers, which he carries around until something tears it loose.

A more or less companion activity to these jousts with trees and shrubs is wallowing, which seems to occur only during the rutting season. In northern California, I watched elk use stagnant pools full of foul-smelling mud to wallow in. The bull waded into the water and submerged his head and neck; then, kneeling, he rubbed his chest, neck, and face in the slimy mud. All of this took about ten minutes.

In other ranges, elk dig wallows in wet or marshy spots. They thrust their antlers into the damp sod in much the same way they thrash about in brush, tossing their heads vigorously to clear out the dirt. They also use their hoofs to scoop out the wallow. When one is constructed to a bull's satisfaction, he lies down in the damp mud. It has been suggested that the wallow serves to cool off the bull and dampen his ardor a bit. One that has been wallowing is often caked with mud.

William Graf, in his studies of the Roosevelt elk, stated that there is usually a strong musky odor around a wallow, sometimes so intense as to be nauseating. It was his opinion that this was due to large amounts of urine and droppings around the wallow.

Wallowing is mostly confined to old bulls, but how often they indulge in it is not known. Two-year-old bulls are thought to wallow once in a while, but apparently spikes and cows never do.

Another characteristic act of rutting bulls is "grimacing." The neck and muzzle are extended outward and slightly upward, and the lips are curled back to expose the lower incisors and the dental pad. While petting a three-week-old male calf in the Children's Zoo in Portland,

Grimacing is characteristic of rutting bulls.

This wise old fellow made only one charge to drive off a bachelor bull and then returned to his waiting harem.

Oregon, I observed that it gave this same kind of grimace. I have no explanation for it other than that it appears to be a form of sex play.

When a bachelor bull gets too close to the herd, the harem master charges him. Most of the time this is sufficient to cause the intruder, especially if it is young, to turn and run. The wise old male makes only one charge and then returns to his cows. Should he get involved in a time-consuming brawl or chase, other unmated bulls could make off with his cows with comparative ease.

I became involved in a charge of this type some years ago, and for a few spine-chilling moments I thought I was destined to be skewered on the dagger points of a very angry harem master. When I first saw this bull he had only two cows and a calf with him. Whether or not this was all that remained of a larger group I had no way of knowing, but the alert manner in which he was looking after his cows indicated that he had no intention of losing either one.

Cautiously I moved to a good vantage point thirty yards from where they were feeding in a small meadow. After about twenty minutes one of the cows disappeared into the nearby timber. The bull ran after her but must have had some trouble persuading her to return, for it was several minutes before the pair reappeared. Possibly the reason for the difficulty may have been the young bull that came into view on the edge of the clearing fifty yards away. He looked to be about twenty-eight months old. His antlers were four-point but small and thin. He was obviously no match for the herd master with his massive six-point antlers.

The big bull started forward at a steady, measured pace; the younger moved away in a counterclockwise direction. Suddenly the harem master charged and the youngster fled. They went past me and headed toward the road. A passing motorist saw them and honked his horn. He must have thought they were going to attack him. The harsh sound turned them back, and they headed straight toward me. The young bull turned off and vanished in a dense thicket. The big bull saw me and

The breeding season is no time to get in the way of a bull. This one had murder in his eye as he advanced toward me.

A mock battle this is not. These two bulls are pushing at each other with all their strength. One of them must eventually accept defeat. (Leon E. Stumpff, photographer)

came to a crashing halt ten yards away. He looked straight at me. There was murder in his eyes. He seemed to be deciding whether or not to vent his wrath on me. I took his picture while he stood there looking at me, but it was mostly a reflex action, for what I was really interested in was a place to go if he decided to charge. A clump of small trees ten feet to my left offered the only hope of cover, so I started inching toward it. This may have helped the bull decide I wasn't anything he should bother with, for he turned away and went back to his two cows.

There comes a time, of course, when every herd bull must fight for his harem. Inevitably the older bull, as he ages, weakens. A young and more vigorous animal defeats him and takes over his harem. Most clashes between bulls are brief and consist primarily of a head-to-head pushing match. After a few seconds of back-and-forth shoving, one bull, usually the challenger, breaks off the match and runs away.

Nevertheless, these fights can turn into real life-and-death struggles. When a serious challenger approaches, the herd bull, perhaps sensing that this is no youngster to be chased away with a threat, goes to meet him. He carries his head forward on stretched neck; his antlers are held back. The challenger bugles in reply and thrashes about with his antlers.

They move forward on a collision course. When no more than fifty feet separate them, they circle each other. Then they stop circling and charge. Their antlers come together with a resounding crash. They push and twist. Hoofs dig deep into the soil as each strives mightily to upset the other and get him at a disadvantage. This goes on for a minute or so with neither bull gaining. They separate and then come together again. Suddenly, with a great effort and twist of his head, one bull throws his opponent to one side, charges into his flank, and knocks him off his feet. The loser accepts defeat and runs off into the timber.

A vanquished bull does not necessarily consider the decision final. There are instances of bulls losing their harems and then winning them back again before the breeding season is over. It would seem that, when contesting bulls are somewhat evenly matched, the outcome may be decided by some slight advantage which could just as easily go the other way on the next meeting between the two.

Sometimes serious injury or death results from these encounters. Bull elk are tremendously strong, and their massive antlers are vicious weapons. The fact that some elk are badly injured while fighting is not nearly so remarkable, I think, as the fact that there are not more fatal or crippling injuries.

Battles have been reported in which the antlers of one bull were broken off. Other times the loser's antlers have been ripped loose, taking palm-sized sections of the skull with them. And, as with deer, fighting elk sometimes get their antlers so entangled that they can't get free. Then both die. Several fatalities which occurred while a bull was merely protecting a choice bit of food prove that the sharp points of an antler can be lethal. Quick, efficient thrusts of an antler pierced the abdomens of two cows that later died; in a similar attack two calves were killed outright. There are also two reported cases of a cow being killed when an antler point pierced her forehead and entered the brain.

Rutting begins in early September. Normally a cow elk breeds at about twenty-eight months of age; however, there are many examples of sixteen-month-old females that have been bred and produced their first calves at about two years of age. Breeding capabilities of females so young seem dependent upon the severity and duration of their first winter. If the winter has been short and mild, a much larger percentage of yearling females will breed than if the preceding winter was a bad one. In one section of New Mexico, 61 per cent of the yearling cows were found to be pregnant. Females are most prolific at six to seven years of age, which is considered the prime period of an elk's life. A captive cow elk gave birth to a calf when she was seventeen years old, which indicates that healthy mature cows in the wild probably can breed successfully all of their lives, since their life expectancy is apt to be somewhat less than seventeen years.

A bull and his cow in one of their more peaceful moments.

Bull elk are capable of successful matings as yearlings sixteen months old. This has been substantiated by microscopic examinations of yearling sperm and by experiments in which cows confined with yearling bulls have produced calves. There is little opportunity for a yearling to utilize his capabilities, however, as he is not strong enough to compete with the larger bulls. As a matter of fact, a bull elk must go through several frustrating rutting seasons before his size and strength enable him to become an active breeding bull.

Oestrus occurs at approximately twenty-one-day intervals during the rut and lasts for about seventeen hours. The period during which a cow is receptive to mating is quite short, and scent is important in alerting the bull. Without the cow's cooperation he will be unsuccessful. He approaches her from the rear with his neck outstretched and places his chin on the cow's back near the tail to see if she is receptive. If she is, mating takes place. Rebreeding has been noted, sometimes less than a half-hour after the first mating, sometimes as long as seven hours later.

Pregnancy rates in cows of breeding age usually run between 85 and 90 per cent. Successful matings, as well as successful births, depend to a considerable extent on the quality of nutrition in the forage available to the cows.

The intensity of the rut diminishes early in October, and by the latter part of the month the season is over. The herd bulls are no longer in prime condition. For a month or more they have been able to eat only sparingly, for keeping their harems intact and untouched by opportunistic bachelors leaves them little time for anything but police work. While the members of the harem are fat and healthy at the end of the rutting season, the herd bulls are thin and tired; their heads droop, their foot-steps drag. They bear little resemblance to the proud and arrogant males that took over the cow herds in early September.

Today, elk are hunted legally in Arizona, Colorado, Idaho, Montana, New Mexico, Oregon, South Dakota, Utah, Washington, and Wyoming.

Occasional limited seasons have been opened in California, Michigan, Nevada, Oklahoma, and Texas.

In states with small populations of elk, a limited number of hunting permits are issued. In other states, elk hunting is confined to resident hunters; in only a few are nonresident licenses also issued. The present status of elk hunting speaks well for modern game management practices—almost too well, in fact, for in many elk ranges special seasons on antlerless elk have been necessary to reduce herds that have over-populated their range.

In theory at least, elk hunting is a sport for the hunter who is primarily after a good trophy in the form of a mountable head. The tasty meat of the elk is an added bonus. Most elk-hunting seasons are either during or just after the rutting period, when the breeding bulls are in poor physical condition. While this undoubtedly affects the palatability of the meat, it is still good. At least the few samples that I have had were excellent. Measured by the amount of time the average elk hunter spends in the field, he could buy the best beef a lot cheaper than he can kill an elk. Like many averages, however, this one can be misleading. There are many *good* elk hunters who are consistently successful, and the meat they obtain becomes an important part of their winter food supply. On the other hand, the casual elk hunter does not usually fare so well.

Actually, there are far fewer elk hunters than deer hunters, as shown by the national figures for animals killed in 1967: elk, 81,368; deer, 2,087,406. This difference is so great partly because elk cannot be found near large population centers, and partly because elk-hunting is extremely strenuous and often costly.

There are few, if any, huntable elk found in *easy* country; the land is mostly steep, rugged, and remote, the weather often severe. In the remote elk range in the wilds of Montana, Idaho, and Wyoming, for instance, pack strings and guides do a big business. Four-wheel-drive vehicles are now quite popular. Some of these are equipped with power winches holding several hundred feet of small cable. This is used primarily to move the vehicle if it gets stuck, but is also valuable for bringing in an elk carcass.

An experienced hunter once ruefully told me that, no matter where you shoot an elk, he will make it to the nearest canyon and fall all the way to the bottom. They are big animals and, even when skinned and quartered, are difficult to retrieve by manpower alone. A pack horse or power winch can prevent a lot of aching backs.

Elk hunting involves two basic techniques, still-hunting and the drive. For a drive, several hunters go together. In hunting country, which consists of open meadows and bare side hills and ridges mixed with dense timber, some of the hunters take stands overlooking the cleared areas while the others move through the cover in a direction calculated to drive the elk toward those on stands.

Still-hunters find a good overlook and sit motionless. Other hunters in the vicinity often act as involuntary drivers. I heard of one hunter who sat on the same stump all season long for six consecutive years and finally connected with a fine six-point elk. He deserved it for his patience, if nothing else.

If the season is open during the rut, a bull can be located by his bugling. There are manufactured elk calls which look like overgrown whistles; and these are frequently used to bring a bull in to the hunter. The only one I have ever heard was home-made, and when Lester Abbie demonstrated it to me one chilly moonlit night we got a quick answer.

It is sometimes possible to follow fresh elk tracks and get within rifle range of the quarry if the wind is blowing from elk to hunter. Some horseback hunters prefer to ride along until they spot a bull within range and then dismount to shoot.

Regardless of what method of hunting is followed, only large-caliber (.270, .30-06, .300), high-velocity ammunition should be used. Elk have tremendous stamina and when wounded, even severely, can travel long distances.

Every dedicated elk hunter dreams of someday getting a mighty bull that will be the biggest and best ever killed. The Boone and Crockett Club keeps records of the large big-game animals killed. At first, trophies were judged on length of antler beam and maximum spread. In more recent years, an evaluation system has been adopted which takes circumference of beam and symmetry into account. The score is the result of multiple measurements that are evaluated as points. On this basis the widest spread does not necessarily produce the highest score.

The number-one elk in the club's 1964 publication, *Records of North American Big Game*, had a length of beam of 55⅝ inches on the right side and 59⅝ inches on the left. Inside spread was 45½ inches. Circumference at the smallest place between first and second points was 12⅛ inches on one side and 11¼ inches on the other. There were eight points on the right antler and seven on the left. The animal was killed in Colorado in 1915. The number-two bull had the same number of points but longer beam, 61¾ and 61¼ inches, and an inside spread of 47 inches. However, the antlers were not so massive. It was killed in Wyoming in 1890 and is now on display in the Jackson Hole Museum.

Winter

AN ESTIMATED 75 per cent of all American elk live in the Rocky Mountains, where winters normally include long periods of snow and cold weather. Another 15 per cent or so inhabit the Olympic Peninsula in Washington and the coastal range in Oregon. While winter in these two regions is not as severe as it is in the Rockies, there is usually enough snow to force some vertical migration. At infrequent intervals deep snows fall in these areas, causing much hardship and suffering in the elk herds. Such a situation exists as I write this. An unheard-of two to three feet of snow has fallen at sea level on the central Oregon coast, with probably twice that amount at higher elevations in the coast range. If the snow pack remains for any length of time, many elk will starve. While this is unusual, winter is nearly always a bad time for elk, and some losses are normal.

After the rut, the older bulls drift away from the cow herds to congregate in groups of a dozen or so. However, I have observed many of them alone at this time of the year. Spike bulls usually return to the cow herds, along with some two-year-olds and a few three-year-olds.

During migration, routes overlap, and small herds join together. As the winter range is usually smaller than the summer one, these groups tend to stay together, banding with others to form large winter herds.*

*In *The Elk of North America,* Olaus J. Murie points out that people who fed elk year after year on their wintering grounds in the National Elk Refuge learned to recognize some individual animals by their abnormalities. Murie concluded that some elk repeatedly returned to the same area to spend the winter—*The Editor.*

Deep snow with a frozen crust is the elk's worst enemy. Crust that is strong enough to hold them enables them to cover a large area in search for food. If the crust will not bear their weight, they have trouble both moving about and digging through the snow to forage. Under these conditions they can starve or become easy prey to coyotes, wolves, and cougars.

In deep snow the young elk, unable to get through on their own, are the first to suffer. The best they can do is follow in the paths made by older and larger animals, but then they don't get a chance at the available forage until after the others have fed.

Mature elk can move through 40 inches of loose snow without excessive difficulty. If it is lightly packed or thinly crusted, 30 inches is about their limit. It has been suggested that 48 inches of snow is as much as most elk can get through efficiently. Calves and older animals in a weakened condition are limited to about 30 inches. In deep snow, elk bunch up and travel in single file. Various ones take turns breaking a trail through the snow, but this is probably a haphazard or accidental selection.

Elk often push through 12 to 18 inches of snow with their noses to feed; they paw their way much deeper—as much as 36 inches—when necessary. It appears that somewhat less than this, 30 inches or so, is enough to cause elk to browse more.

Most elk that winter on ranges with inadequate food supplies suffer to some extent from malnutrition before the cold months end. The extent of the deficiency is directly related to their physical condition at the beginning of the winter and to the quality and quantity of available forage. During the last thirty days of winter, reckoned according to the calendar rather than the weather, Jackson Hole calves lost almost a pound a day on the average, and both adult cows and bulls lost almost two pounds a day.

When food is in extremely short supply, elk sometimes stuff themselves with coarse woody browse and too much coniferous growth, and malnu-

Heading for the winter range.

trition results. Malnutrition is the principal cause of elk deaths in winter, although the animals may not actually die until after winter is over. The new spring plants are not rich enough in food value to restore the elk to health and they may expend more energy obtaining food than they gain. New plant growth also acts as a laxative, which further weakens the animals.

It has been suggested that winter losses are the worst a herd can suffer, because both the animal and the precious winter range are wasted. By contrast, the bulls taken during a post-rut fall hunting season have done their duty to perpetuate the herd and have then furnished food and sport to the hunters. This means that there is more forage for the remaining animals; thus some are saved that otherwise would starve and die.

Pregnancy rates of from 85 to 90 per cent, and cow-calf ratios of around 2 to 1, indicate approximately a 40 per cent loss of calves somewhere between the breeding season and the following summer. The causes of such losses are still under investigation, but the most logical one is malnutrition due to a lack of winter forage. Either weakened cows fail to carry their pregnancies to term or, if they do, the calves are too weak to have much chance of survival.

Parasites do not seem to be a major cause of elk fatalities, although they may be an important contributing factor when the animals are weakened by malnutrition. The winter tick, *Dermacentor albipictus,* is common in Rocky Mountain elk and Roosevelt elk. Severe infestation was reported in the Manitoba elk of Riding Mountain Park in Manitoba, Canada, when elk populations were almost double the estimated carrying capacity of the range. When herds were reduced to 50 per cent of estimated carrying capacity, evidence of winter ticks was found on only 20 per cent of the animals examined.

Winter ticks are a seasonal scourge. Actions of an infested elk indicate that the ticks become extremely bothersome in late March, but they undoubtedly attack long before that. They continue to be a problem until

As the snow gets deeper, elk have a harder time getting through it.

May, when the female ticks drop off the elk to lay eggs. When heavily infested, an elk does a lot of scratching with its hind hoofs. Sometimes enough hair is worn off the neck by scratching to give it a rather odd appearance. John E. Schwartz reported that Roosevelt elk in the Olympics were infested with winter ticks in all months of the year.

The lungworm, reported to be one of the most widespread and serious parasites infecting Olympic elk, is apparently of little consequence for elk in Jackson Hole. Other parasites that live in or on elk include giant liver flukes, sarcosporidia, tapeworms, intestinal worms, biting lice, and botfly larvae.

Mites that cause scabies have been found—most often, strangely, on mature bulls. Adult cows are affected at times, but younger elk, including calves, are rarely scabby. Scabies, which is transferred from one host animal to another, occurs in winter, when the animals are in poor physical condition. It disappears in the spring, after rich new forage appears. (This may explain why scabies is found most often on bull elk, worn out by the rutting season.) It causes loss of hair, and, if the weather is extremely cold, the animals suffer. It can become so severe that death results, but it is doubtful that all dead elk found with scabies die from it; other diseases in conjunction with, or aggravated by, scabies may be the cause.

Elk are susceptible to a number of diseases and ailments, most of which seem to be relatively unimportant to the health of the herds. Necrotic stomatitis is one disease, however, which under certain conditions has a marked effect on elk herds. It is usually fatal, although there are indications that some of the older animals recover.

When hay is fed to elk, as it is on the National Elk Refuge, or when the animals are forced to feed on heavy browse, seeds, stiff stems, coarse forage, and splinters, these get jammed between the teeth or stuck in the gums and may cause punctures and abrasions in the mouth. In damaged spots, infection can set in; the bacterium known as *Actinomyces necrophorus* causes necrotic stomatitis.

The first sign of the disease is a droopiness and general lassitude on

This young bull is pawing away the snow to get at the browse.

the part of the affected animal. Emaciation follows, with labored breathing. In the final stages the elk lies down and is unable to rise, and within twenty-four hours is dead.

Because elk and other animals always appear so much at home in their wild surroundings, we do not often think of them falling, drowning, or otherwise getting hurt or killed accidentally. The truth is that accidents to elk are not uncommon.

Elk are good swimmers, but drownings do occur. In the fall, when ice covering the lakes is not strong enough to bear their weight, they may fall through and drown. Seventeen died at one time in Jackson Hole Lake in the Grand Teton National Park in such an accident. Calves sometimes drown while crossing stretches of treacherous water.

During a post-mortem examination of an Olympic elk, a spruce twig 1½ inches long and ¾ inch in diameter was found imbedded in the lower part of its left lung. Possibly this was part of a snag the animal impaled itself on in some manner. In a similar accident a yearling cow was killed when a sliver of wood, 11 inches long and 1½ inches in diameter, pierced a lung.

Elk occasionally become entangled in barbed wire and are unable to escape. Forest fires and snowslides kill a few, and once in a while one will lose its footing and fall from a cliff. I know of one case where a big bull was mired down in a mudhole in Yellowstone National Park. It was there for a couple of days before it finally managed to get out. By that time it was in such poor physical shape it either died from exhaustion or was killed by coyotes.

It probably doesn't happen often, but on June 1, 1968, an elk was hit and killed by a car on U.S. Highway 97 in central Oregon. This was an especially odd accident, for at that time of year the elk in central Oregon are usually following the receding snow line up the eastern slope of the Cascades some fifteen miles west of the place of the accident. Furthermore, I have never heard of another elk being seen along that particular stretch of highway.

121

Crippling and wounding of elk by hunters, while not properly classifiable as accidents, take their toll. When I visited the National Elk Refuge in Jackson Hole one early spring, I saw a surprising number of elk bearing the effects of what were probably gunshot wounds. Several were hobbling around on stiff, useless legs, and one had the lower part of a foot missing. Probably more cripples had been around earlier in the winter. Each morning there were usually several that did not survive the night.

Predators do not seem to present much of a threat to elk. In national parks where herds are protected, populations increase beyond the carrying capacity of the ranges despite the fact that predators are also protected and are allowed to prey on the elk herds to whatever extent they can. Coyotes, bobcats, and bears take an elk calf when they find one, but they avoid tangling with the cow: the hoofs of an angry female elk are potent weapons. Coyotes frequently kill elk during the winter, but these are usually animals weakened by disease, injury, or malnutrition.

A band of cow elk have been known to trample a coyote to death. On the other hand, a pack of coyotes have attacked and killed a single elk. Among California's tule elk, coyotes that approached a herd too closely were quickly chased away. Cows did most of the chasing, but on one occasion several spike bulls pursued the intruder.

Bears seldom bother a mature elk but have been known to kill young ones. Even attacks on calves do not always prove successful. It was reported from Yellowstone National Park that an irate mother elk chased a black bear up a tree. The cow went back to her calf, and after a few minutes the bear tried to sneak down. The alert elk rushed the bear and sent it back up the tree. The bear made several more unsuccessful attempts to escape, but the cow kept it there for several hours before she walked away with her calf.

Another bear was not so fortunate. It either attacked or failed to avoid a big bull and was quickly skewered on the sharp points of the

The black bear seldom tangles with an adult elk. An unprotected calf is another story.

bull's mighty antlers. Another bull elk in Arizona's Oak Creek Canyon must have been irritated by a Volkswagen that he found blocking his path. He butted the car, ripped through a door and window, and gored the driver in the chest, breaking two of his ribs and puncturing a lung. On Afognak Island in Alaska there are Kodiak bears weighing as much as 1,000 pounds. Nevertheless, losses of elk there as a result of bear predation appear to be negligible, as indicated by a phenomenal increase in the elk population.

In the early days, wolves were effective predators of elk and seemed to kill them with comparative ease. But there are not enough wolves left in many areas of this country for them to help keep the rising elk population in balance with its available food supply. Some elk, both calves and adults, are taken by gray wolves in Jasper and Banff National Parks in Alberta, Canada. Reports from this area indicate that a single wolf can kill an elk but that the elk can protect itself if it is in such a position that a wolf can attack only from the front. It can also protect itself in deep soft snow, in which a wolf flounders. If elk can be driven onto the insecure footing of glare ice, wolves kill them easily.

The cougar seems to be the only predator in the United States which consistently preys on the larger elk. John E. Schwartz cited an example of a yearling cougar killing an adult elk in the Olympics. The elk appeared to be in healthy condition and was estimated to weigh about 600 pounds. A few hours after the kill was made, the cougar was tracked down and shot. It weighed 76 pounds. This seems to be quite a remarkable feat, but no more so than reported killings of mature mule deer by 25- to 30-pound bobcats. The most logical explanation to me is that they drop onto their prey from above and avoid the dangerous hoofs.

Schwartz also mentioned that ten cougar kills were discovered on the winter ranges during 1936–1938. This was about a tenth as many elk as were found dead from malnutrition, disease, and undetermined causes. It is likely that cougars prefer to prey on deer, since their smaller size makes them much easier to kill.

Cougars prey on elk, but they seem to prefer the more numerous, and more vulnerable, deer.

For animals so large, and equipped with such formidable weapons as sharp hoofs and massive sharp antlers, elk are surprisingly timid around man. I have mentioned being threatened by an elk a few times, but I believe all of these were mostly bluff. Of course, I was also closer than the casual observer need be, since I was after pictures. The times I might have had trouble were during the early calving season and the rut, both of which are periods of emotional peak for elk. At other times the animals, even those in parks, will probably move away when man approaches. I am convinced, just the same, that it always pays to be cautious around a wild animal, particularly one as large as an elk.

A differential sex survival has been noted among elk which has yet to be fully explained. Elk calves show a balanced ratio between sexes which apparently continues through their first two years of life. After that a predominance of females begins to show up. In Jackson Hole, ratios of four cows to one bull have been noted in winter counts. In Colorado a similar winter ratio of sexes was noted. Olympic elk were estimated to be in the ratio of three cows to one bull. This sex differential, it is evident, affects bulls of breeding age.

There seem to be two principal causes. The first results from the rigors of the rut. The physical deterioration of mature bulls during this

125

period is apparently sufficient to be a major factor in causing a substantial number of deaths. Chester C. Anderson, in his report of the elk at Jackson Hole, Wyoming, suggested that the prime bulls that do most of the actual breeding function as harem masters for only one or two seasons. After that they fall victim to winter conditions or become too old to compete with the younger males. The percentage of winter losses among bulls on the National Elk Refuge is three times as great as among cows.

The second cause is the kill by hunters. In states which have cow seasons (states with the most elk), hunters shoot about as many cows as bulls, but since there are fewer bulls the ratio is increased.

Given the opportunity, elk can live a long time. Captive elk have lived to twenty-five years, but sixteen to eighteen years is probably normal. Two eighteen-and-one-half-year-old cows and a thirteen-and-one-half-year-old bull were reported from wild herds in Montana. On the average, bull elk live shorter lives.

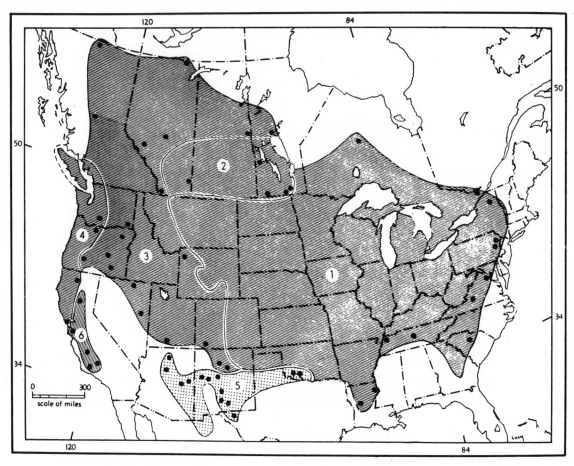

1. *C. canadensis canadensis*   3. *C. canadensis nelsoni*   5. *C. merriami*
2. *C. canadensis manitobensis*   4. *C. canadensis roosevelti* 6. *C. nannodes*

Map of North America giving former range of American elk, as shown in The Mammals of North America, *by E. Raymond Hall and Keith R. Kelson. (Copyright © 1959. The Ronald Press Company, New York. Reprinted by permission of the publisher.)*

The Future of
the American Elk

IN EARLY PIONEER DAYS, elk were found in almost all of the area that became the United States, as well as in parts of Canada, including south and southwestern Manitoba, the lower half of Saskatchewan, all of Alberta, and eastern and southwestern British Columbia. Only the New England states, along with Delaware and Florida, apparently have had no elk populations within recorded history. In the other states along the Atlantic coast, elk populations were found. It is likely that northern Mississippi and northern Alabama had some elk along the Tennessee border, since Tennessee itself was well populated with them. Georgia had a few, as did Arkansas, Louisiana, and Texas, but apparently the terrain over a large part of these states was unsuitable.

A corridor extending southward from central British Columbia through the high, dry country east of the Cascade Range in Oregon and Washington into eastern California, and including most of Nevada, contained no elk. However, comparatively small "islands" in New Mexico and Arizona had them. Ernest Thompson Seton suggested that there might have been as many as 10 million in 1760.

For the American Indian, elk provided choice meat and fine skins for clothing. Ornaments made of the two upper canines, or "tusks," were valued highly by the Indians and worn on special occasions. A garment elaborately decorated with them was said to be worth two horses. In 1801, an illustrated newspaper article told of a visit to an Indian village in southern Montana, where it was estimated that its inhabitants possessed 20,000 elk teeth. This probably does not represent as much of an elk slaughter as it seems, since these decorations undoubtedly passed from one generation to another.

From the elk's great antlers the Indians fashioned tools and utensils. Members of the Lewis and Clark Expedition reported that the point of an antler could be used deftly to remove small chips from a piece of flint or obsidian and shape it into an arrow, spear point, or knife. Single elk antlers were also made into bows.

Early explorers and settlers found elk just as useful as the Indians did. In addition to food and clothing, elk provided fat, which was rendered into grease and candles; their antlers were made into umbrella and knife handles, furniture, candleholders, and glue.

As civilization spread westward, elk and other game provided food for both travelers and settlers, and elk herds in the East were killed off quite early, leaving animals only in remote areas. But even these did not last long. The last native elk in New York is believed to have been killed around 1847, and in Pennsylvania about 1867. As with other native big-game animals, this pattern of extirpation followed closely upon the heels of the westward movement. Here and there in small pockets where unusual habitat provided unusual protection, small herds survived for a while. In southeastern Missouri, for instance, elk were seen until about 1898. However, in general, they disappeared from the East by 1850, from the plains states twenty years later, and from New Mexico and Arizona by 1890.

Once the exploratory phases of the pioneers' westward movement were concluded, towns appeared among the farms, ranches, lumber mills, and mines. Elk were handy for the market hunters who were called upon to supply these communities with hides and meat. Farmers and ranchers, considering these animals prime competitors for the food their domestic stock needed, also hunted them and did not care when they disappeared from the range.

The most pointless slaughter of elk occurred after they had already

Only stringent conservation efforts saved the bison from extinction.

been eliminated from most of the country, as the result of a demand for "elk tusks"—the same teeth so admired by the Indians—as symbols of the Elks, a fraternal organization.

As a result of this use and misuse of elk, only remnant herds existed at the beginning of the twentieth century: in a few mountainous sections of Canada, Montana, Wyoming, Colorado, and Idaho, and along the Pacific coast in southern British Columbia, Washington, Oregon, and California. By 1919, only an estimated 70,000 elk remained in the United States.

About this time conservationists realized that, unless something was done, the American elk would soon be extinct. Those states that still had elk populations closed the season or carefully controlled elk hunting. In some states where elk had vanished, transfers of surplus animals from the herd in Yellowstone National Park provided a nucleus from which sizable populations have grown. New Mexico, which originally had both the Rocky Mountain elk *(Cervus canadensis nelsoni)* and the now-extinct Merriam's elk *(merriami),* supports a growing population of Rocky Mountain elk which were started from elk transplanted there. Arizona has re-established its elk herds the same way. In 1928, eight elk calves from herds of the Roosevelt elk on the Olympic Peninsula were moved first to Kodiak Island and then onto Afognak Island, Alaska, and became the foundation there of a herd that now numbers more than 1,200 animals. Interestingly, elk were also introduced in New Zealand.

131

The American moose above shares some range with the American elk, but the two are not competitive for food.

There are small herds on refuges in several states; in South Dakota, reintroduced elk have increased so much in the Black Hills that there are surplus animals, which are harvested by hunters. Elk transplanted to Michigan and Texas have also done well. Most American zoos have elk on exhibit. They seem to do quite well in captivity; the herd in the zoo in Portland, Oregon, has a reproduction rate as good as, if not better than, its wild cousins, I believe.

Present-day populations are subject to considerable fluctuation, and herd counts in the summer after calving differ from those made in the spring after a hunting season and the hardships of winter. Game management personnel are often reluctant to estimate actual numbers of wild game populations, preferring to determine whether numbers are increasing or decreasing. In Yellowstone National Park and Grand Teton National Park, for example, there are now more elk than the range can handle.

The estimated populations listed on page 135 were collected from many different sources; some were calculated on a basis of the number of reported hunter kills. This is probably a reasonable estimate of the number of elk we now have in North America.

What lies ahead? One must be realistic. It may be pleasant to recall the enormous populations of wild animals of the past, and bemoan their disappearance with the development of our country. There is no possible way, however, to bring back those "good old days," because vast parts of our lands are being used for other purposes and cannot support the wild herds in competition with livestock and farming.

Today, millions of people are finding natural history a fascinating study, and many are expressing great concern for the future of our wildlife animals. The sciences of ecology and game management have developed, and ecologists and game managers are doing a good job of maintaining our wildlife populations. However, it is clear that man himself constitutes the greatest threat to other species.

Not all suggestions to better the lot of wild creatures are practical.

AMERICAN ELK POPULATIONS

In the United States:

Alaska	1,200
Arizona	9,250
California	3,700
Colorado	50,000
Idaho	53,000
Indiana	6
Kansas	60
Michigan	1,250
Minnesota	25
Montana	58,000
Nebraska	100
Nevada	260
New Mexico	11,000
North Dakota	5
Oklahoma	488
Oregon	56,500
Pennsylvania	75
South Dakota	1,600
Texas	1,030
Utah	5,000
Virginia	30
Washington	55,000
Wyoming	71,000
Total U.S. population	378,579

In Canada:

British Columbia	30,000
Alberta	9,000
Saskatchewan	2,000
Manitoba	4,600
Total Canadian population	45,600

TOTAL NORTH AMERICAN POPULATION 424,179

Big horn sheep and elk share some ranges in winter.

Recently, for example, I received a letter from a man who was seriously concerned about deer hunting in the high desert country of central Oregon. Like a great many nonhunters, he believed that our wildlife woes would be ended if all hunting was stopped. What he did not realize was that during the winter deer concentrate in relatively barren desert country in central Oregon, where food is scarce and is replaced slowly. If no deer were killed by hunters, in only a short time—probably less than five years—the winter food supply would be exhausted and substantially all the deer would die.

Elk are not as particular about what they eat as some other species, and consequently in some places they compete with pronghorn, mountain sheep, and deer. In other areas they compete only with deer, but they make stiff competition: elk can browse about 2½ feet higher than deer can. Often the deer are unable to survive. It has been estimated that one elk consumes as much forage as three or four deer. Game management experts must determine whether the land is better used for deer or elk.

There is almost constant conflict between cattle interests and wildlife interests. In some sections, cattle and elk share the same winter and summer ranges. Much of this is Federal land, where livestock is permitted through issuance of a grazing permit. Elk are stronger competitors here, too, for they eat the grass that cattle prefer. The cattle seldom do more than sample browse plants, which elk also eat. But one cow consumes approximately as much food as three elk.

Excessive use by either elk or livestock is bad for the range. Livestock owners consider their animals' need more important than that of wildlife. Game management has the unenviable task of keeping both sides happy without allowing excessive numbers of either cattle or elk to destroy the range.

Elk do not make particularly good neighbors, especially to the farmers.* The usual stock fence isn't even a challenge, although they seem to expend no more energy in jumping one than is absolutely necessary. As a result they are constantly tipping the top pole or top wire, breaking down the fences and occasionally becoming entangled in wire and dying. Farm dogs are no deterrent to hungry elk. In fact, elk have at times displayed a fierce antagonism toward them. A dog accustomed to having livestock run away from it is in for a rude awakening when it takes after elk.

One of the most frequent elk problems facing the Oregon State Game Commission is the elk's winter use of haystacks. Elk-proof fences are too expensive, so eight-foot-high wooden panels have been constructed and loaned to ranchers whose hay reserves have been threatened. When these panels are placed side by side around the base of a haystack, elk can't reach over or jump over. Since the start of this program, some 45,000 panels have been issued!

Haystack raids occur mostly in the winter, but at other times of the year elk may turn their attention to vegetable gardens, pastures, grainfields, and cornfields and often trample other crops that they may not eat.

*According to Olaus J. Murie in *The Elk of North America,* elk are easily tamed, especially if captured when young; but as adults their behavior may be unpredictable. Murie wrote of a rancher in Washington who found some wild elk calves and raised them by hand. They scattered over the range with the cattle in summer and returned to the ranch when the cattle did. However, state laws forbid the taking of elk except during the hunting season, and their unpredictability as captives makes them dangerous to their owners.—*The Editor.*

The picture of contentment.

The Monarch at rest.

It has frequently been suggested that artificial feeding would solve the problems of crop damage and winter food shortages. It isn't quite that simple. Such feeding is expensive. It also induces semidomestication and may make the elk become reluctant to forage for themselves. Furthermore, concentration of animals encourages the spread of disease and parasites.

The range, which in the first place is inadequate for the number of elk on it, suffers further from feeding programs. Large herds of elk destroy most of the surrounding vegetation and thus open the way for soil erosion. The ground becomes compacted by their ceaseless walking about, and future plant growth is inhibited.

The longest continuous artificial-feeding program has been in effect on the National Elk Refuge near Jackson, Wyoming. It started in 1909, when 20,000 to 30,000 elk migrated into Jackson Hole valley, overrunning most of it because their traditional wintering grounds had been taken over by cattle.

With ranchers facing complete destruction of their hay crops, residents of Jackson came to the rescue with hay and labor, and the Wyoming state legislature appropriated 5,000 dollars to feed the elk. In 1911, the United States Congress appropriated 20,000 dollars. The following year, Congress established the National Elk Range. By 1942, public land withdrawals and purchases had increased the refuge to about 24,000 acres—a size believed sufficient to maintain the wintering elk population. But the winter problem still exists.

Summer ranges in the surrounding country, which include both the Grand Teton and Yellowstone National Parks, could support many thousands more animals with natural foods than the already overused winter range can. At this time, the only solution to the problem seems to be herd reduction and artificial feeding.

A couple of years ago I visited this refuge in March, when 6,000 elk were being fed hay. We rode a simulated hay wagon through part of the herd. There seemed to be more than enough hay for them. At least,

140

Hay is scattered on the ground to supplement the food supply on the National Elk Refuge, in Jackson Hole, Wyoming.

when they stopped eating and lay down nearby there was still a lot of hay left on the ground. However, the quantity dropped may have been intended for two feeding periods.

Game managers have successfully increased elk numbers in areas where they had been eliminated or reduced to a bare minimum. Given the opportunity to control populations, game management practices can maintain maximum herds of healthy animals without damage to range.

With what we now know it seems to me that the future of elk in this country depends upon only one thing: How much suitable land are we willing to let them have?

Rocky Mountain elk, Cervus canadensis nelsoni *V. Bailey.*

American Elk
Classifications

Within historical times there have been two species and four subspecies of elk described in North America. Two of these disappeared within the past hundred years, and four remain with us today.

I have obtained the following names and ranges from *List of North American Recent Mammals* by Gerrit S. Miller, Jr., and Remington Kellogg (1955). I have added some common names and have given the extension of ranges resulting from recent transplants.

Extinct American Elk

Cervus canadensis canadensis Erxleben: Eastern elk, Canadian elk, or wapiti. Range: formerly distributed from southern Quebec, southern Ontario, south shores of the Great Lakes, Minnesota, North Dakota, and southern Alberta, southward at least to northern Georgia, Tennessee, Arkansas, and Oklahoma.

*Cervus merriami** Nelson: Merriam elk or wapiti, Arizona wapiti. Range: formerly distributed from White Mountains south to Chiricahua Mountains in eastern Arizona; eastward in southern New Mexico through Mogollon group of mountains west of Rio Grande to Sacra-

*Although the now-extinct Merriam's elk, *Cervus merriami,* has been ranked as a full species by some taxonomists, others believe it was a subspecies of *Cervus canadensis* and should be so classified. The living tule elk, *Cervus nannodes,* is thought by some taxonomists to be a subspecies of *Cervus canadensis—The Editor.*

145

mento, White and Guadalupe Mountains east of Rio Grande; and southward in Texas to southern part of Guadalupe Mountains.

Living American Elk

Cervus canadensis nelsoni V. Bailey: Rocky Mountain elk or wapiti. Range: Rocky Mountains, from north-central New Mexico to northwestern Alberta and northeastern British Columbia, Canada; southward through Idaho into Utah and Nevada; westward to northeastern Oregon and eastern Washington.

Introduced into Arizona, California, Texas, South Dakota, and Michigan. Some other states have small herds in refuges or parks.

Cervus canadensis manitobensis Millais: Manitoba elk or wapiti. Range: southwestern Manitoba, mostly in Riding Mountain region, and central Saskatchewan, mostly in parkland at northern edge of Great Plains region.

Cervus canadensis roosevelti Merriam: Roosevelt elk or wapiti, Olympic elk. Range: western slopes of Cascade Mountains and thence to coast in Washington and Oregon, and southward in humid coast belt and among inner coast ranges to north side of Golden Gate and San Francisco Bay, in Marin and Sonoma counties, California; east to vicinity of Mount Shasta. Also, southwestern British Columbia, especially Vancouver Island. Introduced on Afognak Island, Alaska.

Cervus nannodes: tule elk, valley elk, California wapiti, dwarf elk or wapiti. Range: prior to 1860, nearly entire San Joaquin and Sacramento valleys, especially the lower parts; north at least to Butte Creek, in Butte County, and south to vicinity of Bakersfield, Kern County; west through southern inner coast ranges as far as plains of Cuyama Valley, in San Luis Obispo County and extreme northern Santa Barbara County, also west to near Hernandez, San Benito County, and to south end of San Francisco Bay in Santa Clara County, California.

146

Roosevelt elk, Cervus canadensis roosevelti *Merriam. Light body coloration is typical in late winter.*

Tule elk, Cervus nannodes. *This animal is smaller and lighter in color than the Rocky Mountain and the Roosevelt elk.*

The present population of tule elk is probably under 400 animals. Between 30 and 40 of these are in a captive herd on the Tule Elk Reserve State Park near Bakersfield, California. The Cache Creek herd, a transplanted free-roaming herd of approximately 80 head, is located in Colusa County eighty miles or so northwest of Sacramento. The largest segment of the present tule elk population, between 200 and 300, lives in California's Owens Valley, on the east side of the Sierra Nevada Mountains. These elk are wild and roam freely throughout the valley, which is about fifty miles long and ten miles wide. However, Owens Valley was not a part of the original tule elk range. In 1933 and 1934 the nucleus of this herd was moved there from areas west of the Sierra Nevadas.

The easiest way to identify a subspecies of elk today is by the locality in which it is found. There is very little overlapping of range. But where ranges are adjacent, more than one subspecies may be found.

There are some physical differences between the subspecies, but they are not always distinct. Tule elk are much smaller and lighter in color, with a tendency to light buff. The Roosevelt and Rocky Mountain elk are dark brown or black.

Roosevelt, Rocky Mountain, and Manitoba elk are similar in appearance and could be easily confused unless some of the subspecies characteristics are well defined. The Manitoba form is dark and has smaller antlers. Roosevelt elk are also darker than the Rocky Mountain elk, which is no doubt a result of the heavily timbered areas in which they are found. (Other mammals inhabiting the heavy cover regions of the Pacific coast show darker colorings than similar species living in more open country.) Rocky Mountain bulls have longer, wider, but less massive antlers than Roosevelt bulls. Among the first ten elk trophies rated by the Boone and Crockett Club, there are no Roosevelt specimens—an indication, certainly, that Rocky Mountain bulls produce the finest antlers.

149

Bibliography

Altmann, Margaret, "Patterns of Herd Behavior in Free-ranging Elk of Wyoming, *Cervus canadensis nelsoni*." *Zoologica,* 41:65–71 (1956).

———, "The Role of Juvenile Elk and Moose in the Social Dynamics of Their Species." *Zoologica,* 45:35–39 (1960).

———, "Social Behavior of Elk *(Cervus canadensis nelsoni),* in the Jackson Hole Area of Wyoming." *Behavior,* 4:116–143 (1952).

Anderson, Chester C., *The Elk of Jackson Hole.* Cheyenne, Wyoming: Wyoming Game and Fish Commission, 1958.

Bailey, Vernon, "Our Noblest Deer." *Nature Magazine,* 30:3:137–139, 188 (September, 1937).

———, "A Typical Specimen of the Eastern Elk from Pennsylvania." *Journal of Mammalogy,* 18:104 (1937).

Bird, Ralph D., "A Three-horned Wapiti *(Cervus canadensis canadensis)." Journal of Mammalogy,* 14:164–166 (1933).

Blood, Donald A., "Range Relationships of Elk and Cattle in Riding Mountain National Park, Manitoba." Ottawa, Canada: *Wildlife Management Bulletin,* Canadian Wildlife Service, 1966.

Boone and Crockett Club, *Records of North American Big Game.* New York: Holt, Rinehart & Winston, 1964.

Brown, Will H., "Winter Management of Rocky Mountain Elk." *Oregon State Game Commission Bulletin,* 23:2:3, 6–7 (February, 1968).

Buechner, Helmut K., and Carl V. Swanson, "Increased Natality Resulting from Lowered Population Density Among Elk in Southeastern Washington." *Transactions of the Twentieth North*

American Wildlife Conference, Washington, D.C.: Wildlife
Management Institute, pp. 360–567 (1955).

Buss, Irven O., and J. David Solf, "Record of an Antlered Female Elk."
Journal of Mammalogy, 40:252 (1959).

Cahalane, Victor H., "Elk Management and Herd Regulation—Yellowstone National Park." *Transactions of the Eighth North American
Wildlife Conference,* Washington, D.C.: Wildlife Management Institute, pp. 95–100 (1943).

Cliff, Edward P., "Relationships Between Elk and Mule Deer in the
Blue Mountains of Oregon." *Transactions of the Fourth North
American Wildlife Conference,* Washington, D.C.: American Wild-
life Institute, pp. 560–69 (1939).

Conaway, Clinton, "The Age at Sexual Maturity in Male Elk." *Journal
of Wildlife Management,* 16:313–315 (1952).

Crandall, Lee S., *Management of Wild Mammals in Captivity.* Chicago: The University of Chicago Press, 1964.

Farb, Peter, *The Land and Wildlife of North America.* New York:
Time, Incorporated, 1964.

Gaffney, William S., "The Effects of Winter Elk Browsing, South Fork
of the Flathead River, Montana." *Journal of Wildlife Management,* 5:427–453 (1941).

Goodwin, George C., "Big Game Animals in the Northeastern United
States." *Journal of Mammalogy,* 17:48–50 (1936).

Graf, William, *The Roosevelt Elk.* Port Angeles, Wash.: Port Angeles
Evening News, 1955.

Grinnell, George Bird, *Blackfoot Lodge Tales.* New York: Charles
Scribner's Sons, 1892.

Hall, E. Raymond, and Keith R. Kelson, *The Mammals of North
America.* 2 vols. New York: The Ronald Press Company, 1959.

Hancock, Norman V., and Jessop B. Low, *Aging of Rocky Mountain
Elk by Dentition.* Salt Lake City, Utah: Utah State Department
of Fish and Game, 1956.

Harper, James A., "Ecological Study of Roosevelt Elk." Portland,
Ore.: Oregon State Game Commission, Game Research Report
No. 1, Federal Aid Project W-39-R, 1966.

Bibliography

————, Joseph H. Harn, Wallace W. Bentley, and Charles F. Yocom, *The Status and Ecology of the Roosevelt Elk in California.* Washington, D.C.: The Wildlife Society, 1967.

Johnson, Donald E., "Biology of the Elk Calf, *Cervus canadensis nelsoni." Journal of Wildlife Management,* 15:396–410 (1951).

Julander, Odell, and Duane E. Jeffery, "Deer, Elk, and Cattle Range Relations on Summer Range in Utah." *Transactions of the Twenty-Ninth North American Wildlife Conference.* Washington, D.C.: Wildlife Management Institute, pp. 404–414 (1964).

Kittams, Walter H., "Reproduction of Yellowstone Elk." *Journal of Wildlife Management,* 17:177–184 (1953).

Mace, Robert U., *Oregon's Elk.* Portland, Ore.: Oregon State Game Commission Wildlife Bulletin No. 4, 1956.

Miller, Gerrit S., Jr., and Remington Kellogg, *List of North American Recent Mammals,* Washington, D.C.: U.S. National Museum Bulletin 205, U.S. Government Printing Office, 1955.

Mills, Harlow B., "Observations of Yellowstone Elk." *Journal of Mammalogy,* 17:250–253 (1936).

Morrison, John A., "Characteristics of Estrus in Captive Elk." *Behavior,* 16:84–92 (1960).

Murie, Olaus J., *The Elk of North America.* Harrisburg, Pa.: The Stackpole Company; Washington, D.C.: Wildlife Management Institute, 1951.

————, *A Field Guide to Animal Tracks.* Boston: Houghton, Mifflin Company, 1954.

Newman, Coleman C., *Roosevelt Elk of Olympic National Park.* Olympic Natural History Association, 1958.

Noback, Charles V., and Walter Modell, "Direct Bone Formation in the Antler Tines of Two of American Cervidae, Virginia Deer *(Odocoileus virginianus)* and Wapiti *(Cervus canadensis)." Zoologica,* 11:19–60 (1930).

O'Connor, Jack, and George G. Goodwin, *The Big Game Animals of North America.* New York: E. P. Dutton & Co., Inc., 1961.

Orr, Robert T., "Notes on the Life History of the Roosevelt Elk in California." *Journal of Mammalogy,* 18:62–66 (1937).

Palmer, Ralph S., *The Mammal Guide.* Garden City, N.Y.: Doubleday & Company, Inc., 1954.

Rasmussen, D. I., "The American Elk or Wapiti—Today." *Transactions of the Fourteenth North American Wildlife Conference.* Washington, D.C.: Wildlife Management Institute, pp. 513–526 (1949).

Schwartz, Charles W., and Elizabeth R., *The Wild Mammals of Missouri.* Columbia, Mo.: University of Missouri Press and Missouri Conservation Commission, 1959.

Schwartz, John E., *The Olympic Elk Study,* U.S. Forest Service, 1939.

Severy, Merle, Ed., *Wild Animals of North America.* Washington, D.C.: The National Geographic Society, 1960.

Skinner, M. P., "Browsing of the Olympic Peninsula Elk in Early Winter." *Journal of Mammalogy,* 17:253–256 (1936).

———, "The Elk Situation." *Journal of Mammalogy,* 9:309–317 (1928).

———, "Horn Shedding in Yellowstone National Park." *Journal of Mammalogy,* 2:172–173 (1921).

———, "Migration Routes of Elk in Yellowstone National Park." *Journal of Mammalogy,* 6:184–192 (1925).

Troyer, Willard A., "The Roosevelt Elk on Afognak Island, Alaska." *Journal of Wildlife Management,* 24:15–21 (1960).

Index

155

Index